PACIFIC ISLAND LEGENDS

Tales from Micronesia, Melanesia, Polynesia, and Australia

Bo Flood • Beret E. Strong • William Flood
Illustrations by Connie J. Adams

THE BESS PRESS

3565 Harding Ave. Honolulu, Hawai'i 96816
808/ 734-7159   www.besspress.com

For our children

Megan, Michael, Elizabeth, and Macey Flood
Paige and Marcus Tweedy

Design: Carol Colbath

Library of Congress Cataloging-in-Publication Data

Flood, Bo.
    Pacific island legends : tales from
Micronesia, Melanesia, Polynesia, and
Australia / Bo Flood, Beret E. Strong,
William Flood
        p. cm.
    Includes illustrations, bibliography.
    ISBN 1-57306-084-4 (hardcover)
    ISBN 1-57306-078-X (paperback)
    1. Legends – Polynesia.   2. Legends –
Melanesia.   3. Legends – Micronesia.
4. Legends – Australia.   I. Strong, Beret E.
II. Flood, William.   III. Title.
GR380.F56 1999   398.2329-dc20

Printed in the United States of America

CONTENTS

MICRONESIA 1

THE MARIANA ISLANDS: GUAM AND THE COMMONWEALTH OF THE NORTHERN MARIANA ISLANDS

PALAU

MARSHALL ISLANDS

FEDERATED STATES OF MICRONESIA

CAROLINE ISLANDS

YAP

CHUUK (LOSAP ISLAND)

MELANESIA   ♦ ♦ ♦ ♦ ♦ ♦ ♦ ♦ ♦ **89**

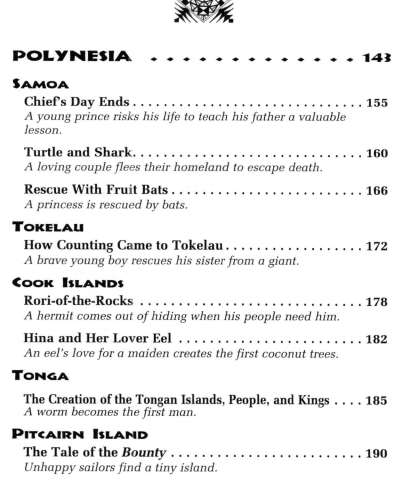

AUSTRALIA 237

PREFACE

In this book we present oral tales in a written format. This is not always easy. When islanders "talk story," it is like a magical dance between teller and listener. Printed words are less lively, like bugs pinned in a display box. The life found in the oral tale takes a different form.

But books can bring stories to everyone. Legends that were once part of an oral tradition become available to readers throughout the world. They cross oceans, continents, even generations. These legends speak a universal language. People everywhere and throughout history wonder about the questions found in these stories: How was the world created? Why do we have both good and evil? Why do families fight? What is the meaning of life and death?

These stories were first told when people gathered together, often in the evening, tired after a day of physical work, lonely for companionship. They were ready to relax. They wanted to be entertained. They were ready to listen to stories that made them laugh at the clever trickster, or even cry with sadness for a tragic life, perhaps similar to their own.

We hope this book will bring alive the magic of storytelling and the wisdom found within these legends. Every traditional story has many different versions. We can present only one version in this small volume. We also include a brief introduction to each region to give you a sense of place and people.

Before you begin, close your eyes and try to imagine the original storyteller. It is dark, the ocean sounds and sweet smells of the jungle surround you. The firelight is flickering. Listen to the story-talk; it speaks to you.

INTRODUCTION

The Pacific Ocean is huge. It is, in fact, the largest feature on the face of the Earth. It covers almost one-third of the surface of the globe. Scattered over this two million square miles of water are over ten thousand different islands. They look like tiny freckles on a very large body, or twinkling stars in the night sky. For the people of these islands, this ever-present ocean is central. It creates their weather. It allows, or prevents, their travel and exploration. It should not surprise you, then, that the ocean, and the creatures of the ocean, appear over and over in their stories. Creatures like giant clams, hungry eels, seabirds, and monster fish become the heroes and villains of a thousand tales.

SETTLEMENT OF THE ISLANDS

The Pacific Islands did not always have people. Many thousands of years ago, people migrated, or moved, there from somewhere else. No one was there writing down all this history at the time. We do have some pretty good clues about the migrations in the Pacific. The earliest **scholars** looked at the skin color or other features of the people to decide where they came from and whom they were related to. More recent studies have looked at the languages of the islands. The use of similar words in different cultures may mean those cultures are related. Even more recent studies have started to look at DNA

scholars
people who are experts in certain fields of study

(part of the genetic code in our cells) hoping to explain the origins of Pacific Islanders.

Most scholars feel that the very first people in the Pacific Islands came from Southeast Asia almost forty thousand years ago. (To read about the settlement of Australia, see page 238.) These dark-skinned people settled in and around the islands of New Guinea. They were the **ancestors** of the Melanesians. They now live on the islands around New Guinea: Papua New Guinea, New Caledonia, Solomon Islands, and Vanuatu. To give you an idea of just how long ago that was, remember that forty thousand years ago was about the time that Neanderthal Man was hiking around Europe.

ancestors
family members who came before, like great-great-grandparents

Much later, only four thousand years ago, a lighter-skinned people moved into these same islands. They began to mix with the darker people, producing many shades of skin in these Melanesian islands. Still later, about 3,600 years ago, **voyagers** from the Philippines and Indonesia moved into Micronesia, first to the Mariana Islands, Yap, and Palau.

voyagers
people who travel by sea

Later, the people from Melanesia moved still farther east into Polynesia. They settled first in Samoa and Tonga. Then they moved north to Hawai'i and Tahiti. Finally they reversed direction and sailed all the way to New Zealand. (Samoans might disagree. Their creation legends place Samoa as the original Garden of Eden, from which all humankind evolved.)

These dates are not exact. What is certain is that people were living on these islands a very long time ago. They lived there before the pyramids were built in Egypt. They lived there before Christ or Buddha was born. They lived there before the Aztecs and Mayans built their **elaborate** temples in Central and

elaborate
created with a great deal of planning and work

South America. In some places islanders built enormous cities, like the mysterious ruin of **Nan Madol** in **Pohnpei**, or the even more mysterious ruin at **Lelu** in **Kosrae**. These island cities were abandoned long ago. They were built, occupied, and deserted by a people about whom we know nothing. The Pacific is still full of secrets.

The **preamble** to the Constitution of the Federated States of Micronesia says that the ocean does not separate these islands. The ocean binds them together. In the same way, all the islands and peoples of Oceania (the Pacific Islands and the continent of Australia) are separated by thousands of miles of open water. They are also bound together by that same ocean. The ocean throughout time has been their highway—for adventure, for seeking new homes at times of **famine** or **typhoon**, or for seeking new wives and husbands to strengthen their clans.

STORYTELLING, AN ORAL TRADITION

Written language did not exist for most Pacific Island people or for the **aborigines** of Australia until recent times. Their histories, **navigation lore**, and legends were part of a highly developed oral tradition of storytelling. Children didn't read books. They listened to their elders, who told them all they needed to learn. They memorized the chants. They studied the dances. This history was passed down through the generations. It is still being told today.

Some of this information was for all the children to learn. It was a kind of spoken schoolroom. Other information was given only to certain people. Healing lore might be passed on to those chosen to be the healers. Navigation lore was the most secret. It was given only to those chosen as future navigators. These stories were often told in secret languages.

Sometimes these stories were shared with an outsider when the teller was afraid the knowledge might otherwise be lost.

The stories in this book are written simply, but they are not simple stories. Many of them came from short poems or chants. Some were recorded hundreds of years ago. We have tried to tell each one just as the first storytellers would have told them, but in modern English. We have "filled in" the story to tell it to you. We have tried to be faithful to the original **theme** and island culture.

theme   main idea

ARRANGEMENT

These stories are grouped by region: Micronesia, Melanesia, Polynesia, and Australia. These geographic divisions were invented by mapmakers. They appear on many maps as tiny dotted lines. These lines don't really exist. One does not stumble upon a "Welcome to Micronesia" sign while bobbing across the Pacific. Some people in Melanesia are quite light-skinned, even though these are the "black islands." Some islands in Micronesia ("tiny islands") are bigger than islands in Polynesia ("many islands").

When Europeans first found these islands, they often gave them names honoring places or persons in Europe. Since most maps were made by Europeans, these names became the ones used by most of the world. Recently, many Pacific Islanders have changed their island names to names in their original language.

Each section includes an introduction to the islands in the region, followed by selected stories. Since there are over ten thousand different Pacific islands, it is impossible to tell even one story from each island without filling a whole library! Instead,

atoll
  low coral island
  often
  surrounding a
  lagoon

we have included a variety of stories and legends from each of the four regions. Even the tiniest **atoll**, like Kapingamarangi, in Pohnpei, may be represented. At least one story of creation is included for each region. Other stories include tales of kings, queens, giants, witches, ghosts, heroes, rascals, the sun and the moon, love and marriage, birds, fish, and other island creatures.

STORIES TO READ AND ENJOY

These stories may be different from other stories you have read. Some are funny and will make you laugh; some are sad, and you may cry. Some are scary and perhaps should not be read alone in the dark, especially if you can hear the waves and wind outside your window or inside your head. They can be read one at a time, or all at once. We think you will enjoy them more in small bites.

If you read these stories in school, you may also study the Pacific Islands in the textbooks *Pacific Neighbors* or *Pacific Nations and Territories*. This book is designed to be used with those textbooks, which can help you understand the themes and settings of the stories.

Close your eyes. Listen to the surf and the wind clattering through the coconut palms. Listen . . . . These are the stories of these islands and their people.

William Flood, Bo Flood, Beret E. Strong
Saipan & Colorado 1999

ACKNOWLEDGMENTS

This book would never have been possible without the generous assistance of many persons and institutions. We wish to acknowledge some of them here and apologize for any omissions.

Our sincere gratitude to the people of the Pacific who have permitted us to share their stories. All of these stories are retellings of their traditional legends.

Special thanks to those libraries, and librarians, who have helped us ferret out tales from places we would not have found without their guidance. Martin Gerbens, Curator of Oceania and Special Collections at Northern Marianas College, helped us begin our search. The Joeten-Kiyu Public Library's Pacific Collection was a valuable resource. The staff of the CNMI Archives, Herbert Del Rosario, "Nomi" Lifoifoi Kosaka, and Tonny Goobaad, were also of great help.

In Hawai'i, librarians at the Bishop Museum and at the University of Hawai'i Special Collections led us to wonderful books and articles from all over the Pacific.

In Colorado, the Boulder Public Library and the University of Colorado library provided valuable resources, including interlibrary loan access to materials across the country.

On Saipan, William "Ron" Barrineau, Executive Director of the CNMI Council for the Humanities, helped in many ways, as did Mar-Vic Munar, writer for the *Marianas Variety*, Elizabeth Drumright, a fellow writer and Pacific enthusiast, and Representative Maria "Malua" Peter of the CNMI Legislature. Dr. Bill Peck from Rota was a constant inspiration. Rita Inos, formerly with PREL and now Superintendent of the Public School

System, shared her stories and her warmth. Connie J. Adams, with her amazing ability to see the pictures within the stories, contributed the beautiful woodcut illustrations.

We are indebted to Northern Marianas College for encouraging our research, especially to president Agnes McPhetres and Provost Roy Fua of the College of Education. Their encouragement kept us going.

On Guam, Dr. Lawrence Cunningham and the staff of the Richard Flores Taitano Micronesian Area Research Center (RFTMARC) were always available.

Several individuals read and commented on this manuscript as it was created. We especially acknowledge Francis X. Hezel, S.J., who along with Megan Flood, John Tweedy, and Kate McGrath made many helpful suggestions.

Many islanders shared their stories, homes, and families with us as we created this book. Very special thanks to Lino Olopai, Cinta Matagolai Kaipat, Latik John, and Mr. and Mrs. Felipe Ruak and their son, Joseph. There were many, many others. Without them, we would have few stories to share.

Finally, we sincerely acknowledge the support and encouragement of the staff at The Bess Press, especially publisher Buddy Bess, and our editor, Revé Shapard. Working with them has been a unique pleasure.

A NOTE ON PRONUNCIATIONS

Pronunciations are provided in the text for names and words not likely to be found in a standard English dictionary. These are suggested pronunciations only; as with any geographical names and foreign language terms, pronunciations may vary, depending on local dialects.

MICRONESIA

Suicide Cliff hovers over the western Pacific Ocean at the northern tip of Saipan. To outsiders, this spot, like all of Micronesia, seems to be a lost and forgettable place in the vast expanse of the Pacific Ocean. But Micronesia has had a very important place in world history. Ever since Micronesia was discovered, the global powers of both East and West have fought over its ownership. From tiny Tinian, which lies next to Saipan, the Atomic Age began.

Micronesia means "tiny islands." This north-western part of the Pacific includes the Mariana Islands, Palau, the low-lying atolls of the Marshalls, **Kiribati,** and the Federated States of Micronesia: Yap, Chuuk, **Kosrae** and Pohnpei, which includes Kapingamarangi Atoll. These islands were the first settled after Melanesia. They were the easiest to reach from the Philippines or other areas from which migration may have begun. Micronesia's location in the western Pacific has always been and

Kiribati
KIH rih bus

Kosrae
kawz RYE ay

still is very important.

Europeans discovered these islands in 1521. People had been living in this part of the Pacific for about three thousand years. Little is known about their pre-discovery history except what is told in legends. In addition, scientists have pieced together information by looking at the things people made and left behind: pottery, pictographs, burial sites, and enormous carved structures and pillars. Many mysteries exist. Giant *latte* columns, tall as trees, still stand on Tinian. The ghost city of **Nan Madol** remains mute and deserted, a "floating" stone city on Pohnpei. Ancient stone paths crisscross islands on Yap and Palau. All of these suggest that at one time large societies lived on these islands. They all disappeared. Only legends tell why.

latte   lat tih

Nan Madol
nahn mah DAWL

Navigators from Chuuk and Yap regularly sailed to the "edges" of Micronesia. They made long sailing trips to trade for seeds, shells, medicines, and pottery. These navigators had great knowledge and skill. Imagine sitting in an outrigger only a few feet high and two dozen feet long. Also imagine sailing across hundreds of miles of open ocean to islands only a few miles wide. European sailors such as Magellan believed this task impossible. Indeed it was impossible for him and other European explorers. Their limited knowledge of the Pacific left them lost and adrift for months at a time.

After those long-ago migrations, there is no history of other people exploring this part of the Pacific until the 1500s. Magellan sighted Guam in 1521 and claimed the Northern Marianas for Spain. Spanish rule did not actually begin until 1668. It continued for several centuries.

Micronesia became a crossroads for both East and West. Spanish missionaries came to save souls. Unfortunately, they and other Westerners brought disease and death. Spanish **galleons** used the Marianas as ports for taking on supplies as they sailed between the Philippines and Mexico, taking silver to Manila in exchange for Chinese goods. In the mid-1800s, whaling ships from Europe and the United States took on supplies in the lagoons of Kosrae, Pohnpei, and Chuuk. Whaling ships brought guns and diseases, which almost destroyed the people. Yap and Palau were less affected. Not until the late 1800s were they "claimed."

The twentieth century brought new changes and new foreign rulers. Japan made Micronesia part of its empire. Japanese companies on almost every island nation grew sugar or **copra**. They mined **phosphate**. Most important, they established Japan as the strongest military power in the Pacific.

The Japanese navy and air force attacked and bombed Pearl Harbor in Hawai'i. As a result, the United States entered World War II. The fight against Japan began. War affected every part of the Pacific.

Micronesia became the final scene of a bloody struggle to break Japan's military power. A surprise air attack in Chuuk destroyed most of Japan's navy. In 1944, Saipan fell. The final battle on Saipan was fought at the northern end of the island beneath Suicide Cliff. Soldiers died along the shores as **civilians** leaped to their deaths. Japanese families lined up on this same cliff. Quietly, orderly, the smallest child was pushed over the cliff by her older brother or sister. Family members leaped to their deaths until only the father remained. His task was

galleons
sailing ships

copra
dried coconut meat

phosphate
rock used to make fertilizer

civilians
people not in the military

to run backward to his death.

More death followed. The United States invaded the nearby island, Tinian. From this tiny, once-quiet island, a secret bomb was loaded and flown north. This bomb exploded over Hiroshima, Japan. The history of the world changed. The Atomic Age began.

If you stand today on Saipan's Suicide Cliff, the warm salt wind whips through your hair. Slender white tropicbirds swoop in pairs along the face of this sheer cliff. Below, white surf crashes endlessly against black volcanic rocks. The ocean stretches miles and miles to an empty straight-line horizon.

Imagine for a moment the different people who have stood on this cliff. In Micronesia, so far from any continents, a history of human events continues to affect the history of the world.

Many ghosts. Many legends. Many stories are still told by people who live surrounded by sea, people who live on islands that seem as far away as the stars sprinkled across the night sky. But the whole world throughout many centuries has been touched by the people of Micronesia. Within their stories are human voices that speak to us all.

NORTHERN MARIANA ISLANDS AND GUAM

The Mariana Islands lie only fifteen degrees north of the equator. They are located over three thousand miles straight west of Hawai'i. Like an exclamation mark made of dots, the Marianas stretch north from the equator. The largest island is Guam. It is the farthest south. To the north are Rota, Tinian, and Saipan. Ten more islands, some with active volcanoes, are located still farther north, along with a few **islets**.

The Mariana Islands were governed by Spain from 1500 until 1900. Then they were controlled by Germany and then Japan. After World War II they became part of the Trust Territory managed by the United States. Eventually, Guam voted to become a territory of the United States. The other islands voted to become a U.S. commonwealth.

Today, the Mariana Islands are a favorite vacation spot for Asian tourists. Hotels line the beautiful white-sand beaches.

Although people from many different islands and nations live in the Marianas today, the first settlers were the ancient Chamorros. Historians describe them as peace-loving and playful. Although they fought real wars, they often settled disputes with tests of skill. They had **mock** battles, canoe races, or sling-throwing competitions. They also competed in singing, teasing, and storytelling. Their most famous stories are about the fun-loving trickster Juan Malo. Juan was a poor Chamorro boy. He was considered stupid and lazy. But Juan always outwitted his cruel Spanish master with a clever trick.

During the early 1800s, the Carolinians (**Refalawasch**) sailed to Saipan from several distant islands. Those islands had been heavily damaged by earthquakes and **typhoons**. The Carolinians sailed in outrigger canoes to resettle on the island of Saipan. The Spanish had forced all the Chamorros on Saipan to move to Guam, so no people lived there when the Carolinians arrived.

For both the Chamorros and the Carolinians, the center of life is family. Cooperation and obedience are important. Most important is respect.

islets
very small islands

mock   pretend

Refalawasch
reh fah lah wahsh

typhoons
storms with very strong winds; hurricanes

Traditionally, when a big fish or turtle was caught, the **maga'lahi**, or village chief, was given the best part. Disrespect for people, land, or sea makes the spirits that are within everything angry. In the Chamorro legend "How the Women Saved Guam," disrespect brings drought, famine, and an island-eating fish.

maga'lahi
mag uh la hee

PALAU

Palau is known for the richness of its stories. It is also known for the beauty of its land and ocean. The Rock Islands are considered one of the geological wonders of the world.

If you snorkel in these waters, you will see giant clams that grow to over four feet long. According to myth, from the belly of the giant clam came all of creation!

Snorkel farther. You might also see shy, big-as-bicycles, blue-faced Napoleon wrasse. In the inland saltwater lakes are colonies of stingless jellyfish. They float silently and as thick as tapioca in pudding. If you are really lucky, you might spy a shy dugong, the Pacific manatee. Only a few hundred still exist. Their fragile presence reminds us to take care of both land and sea. The legend of the dugong reminds us that to disobey clan law might mean death or—more noble—being transformed into a new creature.

On land, bold carvings decorate the men's house, or **bai**. It was once the central gathering place for each village. Carvings and drawings tell the story of creation. They also tell tales of trouble, adventure, rewards, and punishments shared by both people and spirits. Although few *bai* still exist, the story carving continues. Carvings are made on wooden boards called storyboards. These are collected and

bai   bay

sold as works of art.

The people of Palau voted in 1978 not to become part of the Federated States of Micronesia. They chose to become a separate country. In 1980 they adopted a constitution. The following year, the first president took office.

Palau's struggle to become a stable and strong nation has been a troubled one. Its first president was **assassinated**. The next president killed himself (or perhaps was murdered). Now, Palau is a fully independent country with "free association" with the United States. It struggles to develop a strong economy. It wants to preserve both its natural resources and cultural traditions. Citizens are encouraged to remember the traditional values of respect for the earth, the sea, and one another.

assassinated
murdered, usually for political reasons

REPUBLIC OF THE MARSHALL ISLANDS

The Marshalls consist of more than a thousand islands and atolls. Most are only a few feet high. Many are so narrow that from anywhere on the island you can see and hear the surf splashing on both sides of you.

On such narrow slices of sand, owning land is very important. People will fight, marry, or perform magic to keep their land. Legends describe how strong magic can make islands grow smaller or bigger, or entirely disappear.

Pandanus, breadfruit, coconut, and fish are the foods that make survival possible. Every part of the coconut palm is used: liquid for drinking (the only water available during a drought), food for eating, and wood for building. The frond branches are thatched to make roofs. During a typhoon, people tie themselves to coconut trees so they won't be blown or washed away.

For the Marshallese, the ocean is a highway. Their navigational knowledge and canoe-building skills are some of the best in Micronesia. Stick charts from the Marshalls show locations of atolls and wave patterns. Navigators memorize these charts and use the information like a "road map" of the ocean.

Loa   loh uh

lia kwe
   lih uh kweh

yokwe   yock weh

Bikini Atoll was the first island in the Marshalls to have people. Legend tells how **Loa**, the creator of the Marshalls, was especially pleased with the beauty of Bikini. Loa said of this atoll, *lia kwe* ("you are a rainbow"). This expression is now used to describe anything lovely. It has also become a greeting: *yokwe*!

Unfortunately, beautiful Bikini atoll and lagoon was selected as the site for the first peacetime explosion of the atomic bomb. All Bikini residents were removed to another atoll. Over twenty-three nuclear tests were made over the Bikini lagoon. Radiation from the bombs made the area unsafe for people to live on. The people of the Marshalls hope to reclaim their atoll.

FEDERATED STATES OF MICRONESIA

Yap, Chuuk, Pohnpei, and Kosrae are four very different island groups that are now one political unit, the Federated States of Micronesia (FSM). They are all part of the Caroline Islands. These are hundreds of islands and atolls scattered like a stream of stars across the equator. All four groups have similar histories of contact with Spain, Germany, Japan, and the United States. Each island nation has different cultures, traditions, and languages. Some say the people on Kosrae wear the most clothes in Micronesia. On Pohnpei's outer island of Kapingamarangi, people wear the least!

YAP

Some of the tallest palm trees in the world grow here. Stretching tall and slender, they curve upward like long giraffe necks reaching toward the sky. Tufts of green fronds sprout at the top like feathers. These long-necked palms line the island's shores. On Yap you can stand on white sand and see unbroken lines of **indigo** ocean and bright blue sky.

Often the world of Yap is quiet. You might hear few sounds from motors or people, just the trade winds. These seasonal winds move like an invisible stream, whooshing through leaves high above, blowing cool sea air across the land.

The sand is hot. Ancient pathways of smooth black stones lead from the shores into the shaded jungle. These old paths invite you to discover spirits long forgotten. Or perhaps they lead to places of magic where people still possess the secret knowledge of **sorcery** and healing. Magic and medicine have always been powerful on Yap.

On Yap, dance remains a **sacred** way to share story. Before stories were written, stories were danced with hands, face, and feet. Lessons from the **ancestors** were chanted. Stories from the Christian Bible are danced. *Mit-mit* is a sharing of dance. It is also a dance competition like the one held on March 1, Yap Day. On this day, dance groups from almost every village compete throughout the day and night!

Stone money continues to be the most important money on Yap. It is the largest money in the world. It is made of large circular discs of limestone carved from secret caves on Palau. Men sailed to Palau in outrigger canoes to **quarry** enormous pieces of stone money. They navigated by the stars. Somehow they loaded their slender boats with limestone discs that

indigo
dark grayish blue

sorcery magic performed with the help of evil spirits

sacred worthy of respect

ancestors family members who have come before, like great-grandparents

mit-mit meet meet

quarry remove from the ground

measured ten to twelve feet across. Then they sailed home over several hundred miles of ocean.

Traditional ways are honored and kept on Yap. Dances are part of village celebrations. A family continues to measure its wealth in land titles and stone money. A child's name is chosen by the grandfather. This name is secret, rarely spoken out loud. It ties a child to family, land, clan, history, and Yap.

Chuuk

Chuuk State includes almost two hundred outer islands in addition to the fifteen main islands in the Chuuk Lagoon. This huge sheltered lagoon is one of the largest in the Pacific. It measures forty miles from one reef to the other. It is enclosed by 140 miles of barrier reef. What an incredible place to fish, snorkel, and scuba dive!

Chuuk means "mountain." Long ago this whole lagoon area was one volcanic mountain. Over many thousands of years, the mountain sank. The fifteen islands that still exist in the lagoon are the tallest peaks of that original enormous volcanic mountain.

Chuukese trace their ancestry back to the beginning of the clan system. This social ranking system was started sometime in the fourteenth century. According to legends, a great leader sailed to the Chuuk islands, bringing breadfruit, which become the main food. He also began a new social structure, based on clans. It included the use of a secret lan-

itang   ee tang

guage, ***itang***. Only chiefs and nobility were allowed to learn and speak this language. A person who knew *itang* could use it to call the gods or spirits. Calling the spirits was necessary to cast spells.

Many Micronesians say that Chuukese magic is powerful. Magicians, healers, and priests can

10

remove evil spirits that are causing sickness or trouble. They can also make medicines and potions. Some can cure illnesses. Others can cause people to fall hopelessly in love.

POHNPEI

Pohnpei Island is volcanic, mountainous, and almost perfectly round. The coastline has no beaches. Within the large 70-square-mile lagoon are dozens of beautiful islets with white-sand beaches.

Pohnpei State includes eight outlying atolls. Not one atoll is larger than a square mile. Like giant steppingstones, these atolls lead southwest to **Mokil** and **Pingelap** and on to Kosrae.

Far south of Pohnpei are the islands and atolls of Kapingamarangi. Polynesians from Samoa settled these islands. Their chief argued with the spirit magician. They disagreed about who owned which island. Magic was necessary to enlarge the main island. People on Kapingamarangi claim to have the smallest islands and the strongest magic.

The mountainous interior of Pohnpei Island is one of the rainiest places in the world, with an average rainfall of over 350 inches a year. It would take a bucket thirty feet deep—taller than a two-story house—to catch all the rain that falls on Pohnpei in one year. With all this water, rain forests grow lush. Waterfalls roar down.

The lowlands of Pohnpei are where people live. They grow crops in the rich soil. In the jungle, ferns grow as big as trees. Birds squawk invisibly in the thick green **canopy**. Ancient spirits watch for wandering humans. In traditional times people would never say a name out loud in the jungle. A spirit might hear the name. Then it could capture the spirit of the person named.

Mokil moh keel

Pingelap ping eh lap

canopy protective covering

The first people settled on this volcanic island about two thousand years ago. The first oral history describes the rulers who built the mysterious city of Nan Madol. Nan Madol includes nearly one hundred artificial islets, fortresses, burial vaults, temples, bathing ponds, and freshwater pools where fish were raised. Some believe the rulers built the city as the mirror image of a sunken city, part of the legendary lost continent of Mu. For several hundred years, until sometime in the 1400s, thirty rulers, one after another, ruled all of Pohnpei. Finally, they were defeated by warriors, most likely from Kosrae, but possibly from some other part of the world.

KOSRAE

Kosrae is the most easterly island of Micronesia. The next stop heading east is Hawai'i.

Just as Pohnpei is round, Kosrae is triangular. Although it is smaller than Pohnpei, its geography is similar. The interior is mountainous, with rain forests. The island's "edges" are flat, with mangrove swamps. But Kosrae has many sandy beaches and many places to swim and snorkel.

Kosrae is known for its flowers and fruits, especially oranges, tangerines, and limes. It is also known for its mysterious history, full of gods, warriors, nobility, and ghosts. During the 1400s this island was unified under one chief. He ruled from the royal city of Lelu. The commoners lived on the main island of **Ualang**. The royalty and their servants lived inside the walled city of Lelu. Like Nan Madol, this royal city was built on a system of man-made canals and coral streets. The city had stone buildings as well as temples and burial vaults.

Today, Lelu is deserted except for spirits and ghosts. Anyone can visit. But people on Kosrae will

Ualang
oo ah lang

12

warn you: be careful! The city is haunted. Indeed, once you step into Lelu, dark walls rise up all around you. Ghosts seem more real than the outside world you left behind.

After you wander in the silence of Lelu, step outside the walled city. Look south across the harbor toward **Tofol**, the "Sleeping Lady." The curving horizon made by the mountains fills the horizon. The mountain really does look like a sleeping lady.

Tofol toh fawl

The legends about this mountain range explain that the gods were angry with a particular woman. To punish her they laid her in the ocean. Then they turned her into the island of Kosrae. The woman was menstruating at the time. Thus the valley between her two thighs contains rich red dirt. In the past, men made special trips to this valley to gather this sacred red soil. The redness in the rock was used to make paint for outrigger canoes.

NAURU

Nauru is a small, very dry island near the equator. The mining of phosphate has made the people of Nauru among the richest in the world. Now that nearly all the phosphate has been used up, Nauruans get their money from property and other investments all over the world.

KIRIBATI

Kiribati consists of several dozen islands, in three groups: the Gilbert, Phoenix, and Line islands. Most of the islands are low, flat atolls. The islands themselves are very small, but they are scattered across almost two million square miles of ocean. After the islands became an independent nation, the citizens selected the name Kiribati, the local way of pronouncing "Gilbert."

The men of these islands were known as fierce warriors. Their weapons included poison spears and shark-teeth clubs. They protected their bodies with suits of armor tied on with coconut rope. This tough covering protected them from head to toe.

Legends from these islands are full of magic and **transformations**. Children use magic as easily as adults. Sometimes they are tricked by their own use of magic.

transformations
changes from
one thing to
another

HOW THE WOMEN SAVED GUAM

Nothing was left to eat.

Children cried from hunger. Their empty stomachs hurt, hurt, hurt as they chewed on scraps of coconut and fish bones.

The taro stopped growing. Even the banana tree hid its red flower, sad because its petals held no fingers of tasty new banana.

The clouds would not drop rain. Wet winds teased, blowing through palm fronds, rattling the **withered** branches. But the winds only laughed and left swirls of dust, shedding no rain on the thirsty island.

"The spirits are angry," the old woman, the ***maga'haga,*** warned. "The people no longer show respect. They take from the earth, take from the sea and give nothing in return. Nothing! No respect for the earth. No respect for the sea, the water or each other. The spirits are angry. Our punishment will come from our selfishness."

The old woman predicted correctly. The people had not taken care of the earth. Now the soil was **barren** and grew nothing. Water had been wasted. Wells had been emptied and now remained dry.

Suddenly a new danger, a new punishment, woke the people. A rumbling deep within the earth split the night's silence. Harder and harder the

withered
dried out

maga'haga
mag uh HAG uh

barren infertile,
unproductive

ground shook.

"What is happening? What is happening?" The people around Agana Bay ran outside screaming. A **hideous** crunching sound grew closer. Something was eating the earth right beneath them! Rocks from the high cliffs tumbled down and crashed into the sea.

"Forgive us, Ancient Ones. Forgive us!" the people prayed.

"We will not be forgiven easily. We will not be forgiven until we show we will change our selfish ways," said the older women. They knew they must **appease** their **ancestral** spirits, their *ante,* the spirit people who could stop the **drought**, the **famine**, and this island-eating monster.

The men grabbed their spears. "Run to the Men's House. Run for your lives!" they cried. Already a loud "WHOOOO" could be heard. Someone was blowing the Great Triton Shell. "Run to the Men's House. The chief is blowing the Great Shell. Everyone gather!"

The men shoved and squeeze under the tall steep roof. Some stood by the side pillars. Little boys stood on their big brothers' backs and peered in. All the mouths were shouting, "Kill whatever is eating our land!" But no one was listening. Words were thrown like stones at each other. Spears were thrust at the darkness. Feet began stamping.

Outside, women young and old waited, shaking their heads. They listened as the men argued about what to do.

At dawn, once again the earth **shuddered**. This time the sound was unmistakable. Monstrous teeth were crunching the limestone beneath their feet, biting and chewing, over and over until finally, they stopped. Silence. No one spoke. And then a child

hideous
painful to the senses

appease
to calm, satisfy

ancestral
belonging to family members who came before, like great-grandparents

ante   AN tih

drought
long period without rain

famine
great shortage of food

shuddered
shook

screamed. "EEEEE, I see it! A monster! A giant bird fish, huge like a whale. EEEE, it swims toward us."

The men rushed to the shore, pushing past the women. "Yes, there it is!" Everyone could see it, a giant parrot fish, a **palakse'**, a monster covered with scales blue as the sky, green as fat mangoes and glowing gold like a ghostly sunset.

palakse'
pal AK sih

Slowly the parrot fish swam out toward the reef. It opened its monstrous mouth. The people gasped. They saw how its teeth gleamed white, each tooth bigger than a man's head. Snap! The parrot fish bit off a piece of reef. Then with one flick of its tail, it swam into the sea cave under the island.

The men walked back to the village, their heads bowed in fear. "How can we capture such a giant fish? One snap and we lose our heads."

At the Weaving Pavilion, the women gathered. They waited until all were present, from the youngest maiden with bright eyes that had first seen the monster to the oldest auntie with clouded eyes hidden in deep wrinkles. As the women waited, they wove long strips of **pandanus**, in and out, in and out. As they wove they began chanting, praying, and thinking.

pandanus
plant fiber used for weaving mats, baskets, and other products

The women watched and waited, all the time weaving, weaving.
Their fingers wove ribbons of leaves.
Their voices chanted prayers of hope while
Their thoughts wove possibilities.

A monstrous parrot fish was eating their island. It was another punishment sent by the old ones. Their angry spirits had sent the drought and the famine. How could they appease the spirits? What sacrifice was required?

WHOOO! The Great Triton was blown again. Back to the shore raced the men, their bodies glistening with coconut oil. Spears clattered against war clubs. Down to the water they scrambled and leapt into their outriggers. Like a school of flying fish, away they sailed, skimming through the waves and over the reef, following the path of the monster.

The women watched and waited, all the time weaving, weaving.
Their fingers wove ribbons of leaves while their thoughts wove possibilities.

They sat in a circle, their backs straight, their heads bowed. Their long black hair spilled over their shoulders, flowing together like a net.

They wove through the night. As the sun lifted above the straight-line horizon, they watched for signs of husbands and sons returning from the hunt. They did not see tiny triangles of sails grow larger and larger, bringing their clansmen home. But what they saw they remembered.

From one of the undersea tunnels between Agana and **Pago** Bay, the giant *palaske'* swam out into the lagoon. It began eating the island. All day the earth shook. All day the monster ate and ate. The monster was destroying the reef and the land just as the people had been because of selfish thoughtlessness. Soon there would be no land left between Agana and Pago, and then—no island, nothing!

"Hurry home," the women chanted. "Hurry home and kill the monster before it devours our island."

Finally, sails appeared on the horizon. Soon the men were climbing out of their canoes. The women

Pago   PAG oh

18

told what they had seen and then asked, "Let us help you hunt the monster. Quickly, now, before it swims to the tunnel's safety."

The men laughed. "Women cannot hunt. Women only chant and weave. What good is that?"

The men stomped back into the bay with nets and weapons. They surrounded the monster, threw their nets and began to pull.

With one slap of its tail, the giant fish sent bodies crashing into the reef and onto the shore. With its mighty teeth it ripped apart the nets and then darted into the tunnel.

The women watched.

Their fingers threaded pandanus while their thoughts wove ideas. And their hearts prayed. What sacrifice did the spirits want? Like a child searching the sand for a seashell, their thoughts searched for an answer.

The men trudged back to the village dragging their torn nets. The women called, "Let us help you mend the nets and prepare for a new hunt."

The men laughed. "Women, what can you do? Even our **maga'lahi** chief's great strength is not enough."

maga'lahi
mag uh LA hee

The wisest woman, the *maga'haga*, shook her head. She waited for the men to leave and then spoke. "Stop, rest your hands. Come with me to Agana Spring. We will wash our faces and refresh our hearts. With clear thoughts we will ask for help from our **maranan uchan**, the skulls of our ancestors."

maranan uchan
MAIR uh nan
OO tsan

But when the women arrived at Agana Spring, they found lemon peels floating in the water. The *maga'haga* knew that only the women of Pago used lemons to scent their hair. This meant that already an opening had been made between Agana and Pago. If the monster kept eating, Guam would soon be gone.

"Hurry, come here to the spring. Encircle the water. I know what our sacrifice must be. Our beauty, our hair. If you are willing to help, bow your head and I shall chop off your hair."

One by one the women walked to the spring, knelt by the cool water and touched their foreheads to the black rock. The old *maga'haga* took out her shell knife, gave thanks, and asked for courage. Quickly she held each woman's long hair with one hand and cut with the other.

"Now we will begin a new weaving."

Again the women wove through the night, their fingers flying faster than the fluttering wings of **fairy terns**. They encouraged each other with songs and stories. Their heads felt strangely light. No long **tresses** hung down their backs. But to everyone's surprise, their hearts also felt light and full of hope, as if a heavy burden had been cut away.

As the starlight began to fade with the morning light, the weaving was finished. "Come, quickly come." The *maga'haga* gathered up the black net and hurried to the shore. "Here we will wait. When the *palakse'*, the slippery one, comes out of the tunnel, we will throw our net over its head and then everyone pull. Pull with all your strength."

The young ones looked up at their mothers, who nodded. "Yes, we can do this. We have woven our courage into one net. The strength of many has become one."

The monster fish swam out of the tunnel. It circled the women. Faster and faster, closer and closer it swam. With its great jaws wide open, it rushed right at the women!

Snap! Teeth bit into empty air. With one great throw, the women tossed the net over the monster's

fairy tern
small seabird

tresses
strands of hair

mouth. "Pull!" yelled the *maga'haga*. The women pulled as one. Giant teeth tore at the net, but the net held as if filled with magic.

"Pull! Pull up!" urged the old one. The monster's scaly body thrashed from side to side. Its tail slapped the sea, splashing waves high into the air. The women held on. The sea became muddy with sand, **murky** with foam. The women began chanting, "Be brave, be strong. Pull!"

murky
not clear

The men heard their voices, grabbed spears and clubs and rushed to the shore. Quickly the monster was dead. Together men, women, and children pulled the giant fish onto shore. They gave thanks to their ancestors and then began a chant, a new song about how the women of Agana wove their beauty into a net of courage and saved Guam. As the people sang, they heaped coconut husks around the fish, cooked it, and ate.

At last every stomach was full. As the rain began to fall, the people knew that both the drought and the famine were over. They lifted their faces to the heavens and then nodded at each other. What happened today, how their island was saved, would be told to their children and their children's children. Remember, show respect. Take care of this island and each other. Only then will this sea and this land be yours and your children's.

WHY MOSQUITOES SUCK BLOOD

nectar
    liquid produced
    by plants

vain
    foolish

*Only female mosquitoes suck blood. Male mosquitoes suck sweet **nectar** but never blood. Long ago a stubborn young man and a **vain** young woman learned important lessons, but, sadly, too late. But not too late for you. The mosquito will tell you. Listen. When she flies near, and you know she will, she'll whine her story in your ear.*

And thus this tale begins its telling.

antes na ti'emp
AN tis na tee IMP

Talofofo
    tal oh foh foh

Tamuning
    tam uh ning

Antes na ti'emp, in the time of the ancient ones, the son of the chief of **Talofofo** heard of the pleasing beauty of the loveliest lady on Guam. This young woman was the chief's daughter of **Tamuning**.

"I must see her. I must! Now! Even if it is just for one brief glance."

His father warned, "Yes, my son, she is as lovely as they say, but she is dangerous. Don't go near. Her beauty will blind your heart and then trouble will break it."

The son laughed. "Father, I want to see her. Only one look, that is all. What danger is there in that?"

"Don't go, my son. It is said that if you walk near the shores of Tamuning, all you will hear is the whining of this chief's daughter. She is beautiful, but with a dangerous sting. I command you. Don't go."

The son disobeyed. He left Talofofo and walked the shores near Tamuning. Soon he heard complaint after complaint carried out to sea on the trade winds.

"Blah, this coconut cream is sour, not sweet. These mangoes are green but not tart. They do not pucker up my lips. This fish is not fresh. Take them away! Take them away!" Whine, whine, whine. Complaint after complaint.

The young man shook his head. He turned to hurry home. But then he heard someone laughing. He felt eyes staring at him. He turned back around.

This stubborn young man from Talofofo gazed into the most beautiful face he had ever seen. Liquid brown eyes stared back at him. Long black hair blew across a face round as the moon, with a glow as golden as sunset. He watched the curve of her hips, swaying slowly back and forth, back and forth as she walked toward him.

His ears became deaf to everything but the sweet sound of her voice as she greeted him. She could have complained that the sky was too high, the water too wet or the sea too salty. He would not have heard. All he could hear were his own thoughts: *I must have this woman as my wife. I must!*

And so they were married. As the tale tells itself, he loved her, was **enchanted** by her, brought her anything she desired. She loved his admiration but only complained that she needed more, sooner, faster. But then, as this sad tale tells, suddenly she died.

The young husband could not bear to be separated from his wife. He refused to leave her even after many days, even though her beauty grew less and

enchanted
charmed

her smell grew more. He stayed by her side weeping until he was nearly blind. Just as his ears once seemed deaf to his father's words, now his nose seemed unable to smell and his mind unable to think.

"Bury her. Please bury her!" begged his neighbors.

"Take a new wife and heal your heart," commanded his father.

But he heard nothing, smelled nothing. All he could feel was the pain in his broken heart. All he wanted was to gaze at her face, now pale and lifeless.

Finally, he knew he must take his wife's body away or his clansmen would steal it. He built a raft. Gently he placed the body in the middle of the raft. Paddling and chanting, chanting and paddling, he started out to sea.

ancestors
  earlier family members, like great-great-grandparents

taotaomona
  tau tau MUN uh

"Spirits of the ocean! **Ancestors** of our clan, help me," he called.

And soon one did. An ancient one, a ***taotaomona***, heard his call. This ancestral spirit changed into a bird, a sleek white tropic bird with a slender long tail that trailed like a whisper. The spirit swooped over the raft and called out, "From a splinter of bamboo, carve a wooden pin as sharp as a needle. Hurry, carve quickly before your wife's spirit slips too far away."

The young man looked up at the bird. Was he dreaming or was the bird speaking to him? The young man reached for his cutting shell and began carving.

As soon as the needle was ready, the *taotaomona* flew down, grabbed it with his beak and jabbed the bamboo into the man's finger. "Hold your hand over her body and let your blood slowly drip, drip, drip over her."

As fresh red blood flowed over the lifeless body, a blush of color returned to the woman's face.

The tropic bird screeched. Never had he seen such a lovely face. Maybe he should take this woman for his own!

The young man **hovered** over his wife. Breath by breath, her gasps for air quieted to peaceful breathing. She opened her eyes and then sat up. She yawned and stretched as if she were simply awakening from a long slumber.

hovered
stayed nearby, in a state of uncertainty

The *taotaomona* swooped between the two and warned. "My power is strong on the sea but weak on the land. To stay human, you must remain here on the raft with the ocean surrounding you." With one final screech, he flew up toward the heavens and disappeared.

At first the two were happy. But soon the air was buzzing with the wife's complaints. "The sea is too salty. This food is too fishy. I must have fresh water, fresh fruit, something new to satisfy my appetite." She glared at her husband. "Even you are beginning to smell like an old crab." She crossed her arms, closed her eyes, and refused to answer her husband's pleas.

The young man did not know what to do. Which way would lead him to his island's shores? A coconut drifted by and then the branch of a hibiscus with a blood-red blossom. It must be a sign. With a splash he dove into the water and swam toward the source of these land signs.

He made it to shore. There he gathered all the fresh fruit he could find and then branches to make a container that would float. Pushing a small raft loaded with papaya, mango, and tart passion fruit, the young husband swam back to his wife. He could see a small dark speck on the horizon and knew it was she, standing and waiting on their raft. But as he swam closer he saw something strange.

Two people were standing on the raft. His wife was in the arms of another.

Enraged, he dumped the fruit overboard, yelling and cursing. Now blind with anger, he rushed toward the two. Just as he was about to leap aboard the raft and plunge his own wooden dagger into the stranger, the man disappeared. His wife screamed, pushed him off their raft, and then paddled quickly out of sight.

Now he was alone in the sea. Overhead, birds circled and screeched, laughing at him. He shook his fist and screamed back. "I am a chief's son, never to be laughed at. Never! I will have my revenge and it will be deadly."

He swam back to shore. There he saw their raft, empty and deserted. He followed his wife's footprints. She was trying to return to her village. Faster he ran. He would catch her before she could seek **refuge** with her clan.

There! Hiding in the grasses that grew thick and tall where the river empties into the sea, he saw his wife. She was crouched beneath a limestone **crag**, hiding her face, hoping to remain hidden.

He ran toward her, his dagger raised high above his head, ready to strike.

She looked up and began whining. "Give me mercy! Certainly I deserve your mercy."

He never hesitated, never asked one question. With one swift strike, he plunged the dagger into her heart.

Her lifeless body fell into the river and was swept out to sea. Her blood flowed into the ocean. With the changing tide, the bloody water was swept back to shore. Each crashing wave washed her blood

refuge
protection

crag
steep cliff

26

back over the beach where it was caught in the tide pools.

There the blood **curdled**. As the power of the sea spirit slipped away, this human blood turned into larvae, the children of mosquitoes.

And thus this tale ends its telling, reminding us that when rain fills the swamps and tide pools, mosquito larvae reappear. Mosquitoes hatch and fill the air. Flying madly from person to person, they search for the secret that can turn them back into humans.

Whine. Whine. Whine. Mosquitoes whisper in our ears. "Give me your blood. I need your blood to be human again!"

Smack! Quick! When you hear a mosquito whining in your ears, remember: Don't be deaf to advice. Don't be blind to forgiveness. Smack! And don't whine.

curdled
formed small lumps

THE CREATION OF PALAU

This story tells how, "before the time of people," a giant clam produced the first creatures on earth. One of these creatures was a giant baby, the first human. But the story says that this baby ate so much there was "nothing for the people." You may wonder where these people came from. The original legend on which this story is based doesn't say. This and other legends were passed from person to person, in spoken form, for many generations. Perhaps the story got changed along the way. Perhaps two different legends were combined to make one story. Or perhaps you can think of another explanation.

In the long ago, before the time of people, the sea was empty. Empty. Spirits under the sea and spirits above the sea were lonely. They longed to share life.

Ucheleanged, the greatest of gods, felt their longing. "Now! The world is ready. Now!" Ucheleanged traveled across the ocean. "Here!" The great god pointed to the darkest part of the sea. From deep within this black unknown, a volcano erupted. Higher and higher the volcano rose, spewing out **molten** rock. Slowly it broke through the sea's surface, raining hot lava and forming a mountain. This

Ucheleanged
oo 'ul yang uth

molten
melted

mountain grew wider and taller until the mountain became an island. Although this mountain was bare, it was not **barren**.

On this mountain's peak, a strange event happened. The power of the sea touched the power of the sky. Afterward, at that very place, sat a giant clam. The clam just sat. Its huge rippled jaws remained shut. Not moving. Not speaking. But growing.

Day after day, the clam continued to grow. Its shell spread long and far. Its sweet, soft middle bulged bigger and bigger, pregnant with life. But the clam could not give birth.

The sea spirits whispered their worries. They sent huge waves across the ocean, whipping them higher and higher. The great clam rocked as the island trembled. Still the birthing did not happen. The spirits screamed out their alarm, sending the sea crashing against the clam. The clam's giant jaws still did not open.

The most powerful of the gods, Ucheleanged, pointed at the darkness beneath the sea. Winds swirled. Waves peaked, curled, and **plummeted**. Thunder roared. **Typhoon** winds smashed against the giant clam. Still the birthing did not begin.

Ucheleanged again pointed to the darkness deep beneath the ocean. An enormous current **coiled** like a giant serpent. Faster and faster it coiled, gathering power to prepare for a mighty strike.

Ucheleanged roared! A monstrous stream of water rolled up from the sea and then across the land. A wall of ocean crashed against the clam. The mother clam, **Latmikaik**, shuddered. And then her giant lips began to open.

The power in the water now tore again through the clam's body. Her shell split fully apart. Her

barren
not able to produce life

plummeted
fell sharply

typhoon
storm with very strong winds; hurricane

coiled
curled in circles

Latmikaik
lat mih kayk

spewed
   came out with
   great force

mouth now gaped open. All forms of life **spewed** out—out into the waters and onto the land. Terns and swifts flew up toward the heavens. They called to the others, "Come. Come out. Be born."

The rest followed. The ghost crabs hurried into dark shadows. Snakes and sea eels slithered to dry holes and wet. Fruit bats stretched black wings as they hung upside down on branches, warming themselves in the sunlight. Crocodiles snapped at slow-moving lobsters. **Dugongs** nudged shy babes toward quiet lagoon waters. Sharks dashed into deep sea caves. Clouds of color divided into two groups of animals. Birds and butterflies flew upward. Reef fish and creatures of the tide pools crawled back to the sea. The ocean laughed with life. The earth fluttered with color. But the clam mother, Latmikaik, was not finished.

dugongs
   large, gentle sea
   animals;
   manatees

This ancient sea goddess, clam mother, **shuddered**. Once again her jaws opened. One more animal, a human child, crawled out. This giant baby was perhaps female (**Chuab**) or perhaps male (**Uab**). The tale is told both ways. But always the story tells how this selfish child brought both disaster and creation to **Angaur**, the world's first island.

shuddered
   shook

Chuab 'wap
Uab wap

Angaur ang or

ravenously
   with great
   eagerness

This child's appetite was monstrous. **Ravenously**, the child ate and ate. The child cared about nothing else but eating. "More, more, more! Bring more food. Hurry! More, more, more."

The child quickly grew into a towering giant. As

30

the giant grew, its appetite increased. Soon there was nothing left to eat. Nothing for the giant. Nothing for the people. Every breadfruit and coconut had been devoured. The sea waters were empty. Even the smallest reef fish had been netted and swallowed.

But the giant demanded. "Bring food! If you have nothing else, bring me your children. I am hungry. I must eat!"

At first the people of Angaur whimpered in fear. But then as their children began disappearing one after another, they whispered, "The lagoon is empty. The jungle has no banana nor breadfruit. Every coconut is gone. We must save our children."

The people waited until the giant was sleeping. Quickly they stacked coconut stalks around the slumbering body and then lit the wood.

The giant woke confused and in pain. He jumped to his feet, but already the burning flames formed a blazing wall that allowed no escape. He stared at the people. For the first time he saw their fear and **anguish**. For the first time he understood how cruel and selfish he had been.

anguish
deep pain or great suffering

"It is right that I die! I have taken with thoughtless greed. Now I must give back." The giant spoke no more. His enormous body trembled. Slowly he toppled down, down, down. Flesh and bones shattered into hundreds of pieces, flying in all directions. Each piece became new land.

The giant's flesh and bones became the many islands of Palau. Each place kept the **characteristics** of the part of the body from which it had come.

characteristics
features

Airai was formed from the head. People from Airai are known for their wit and wisdom.

Airai   ay ray

Ngaraard is where the stomach landed. Here the people are famous for their good cooking and great appetites.

Ngaraard
nguh rahrth

Aimeliik
  ay mel ik

Babeldaub
  bab el thawp

Aimeliik is a part of the big island of **Babeldaub**, where the land is wet and moist. It rains every day. Can you guess? Of course. Aimeliik is where the giant's penis (or the vagina of the giantess) landed. Water regularly flows at Aimeliik.

You might wonder about the people of Angaur. After the fire had burned to ashes, the people searched through the coals. There they found a part of the body. The giant's feet had stayed on Angaur. The brave people of Angaur to this day are known for their swiftness—and their courage!

HOW THE DUGONG CAME TO BE

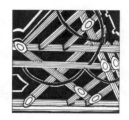

On the faraway island of Palau lived a young woman who carefully kept the ways of the island. She was gentle and kind, moving quietly from one task to another, watching, watching, especially when the children were at play near her home. She was married to a young man who would someday become chief if they both showed themselves to be worthy. They lived in a simple hut **nestled** beneath coconut palms and near the ocean. The constant pounding and crashing of surf against the black lava cliffs was a **soothing**, distant song. But they were not happy. They longed for the sweet sounds of children to fill their home.

As the young woman sat weaving in the shade of the tall, slender palms, her gaze would wander. She watched the fronds overhead swaying and tossing, as if playing with the teasing whispers of the sea wind. Maybe someday her own child would play next to her, laughing as the wind shook the fronds into clatter and dance. Maybe someday.

Each morning her husband climbed the sturdy limbs of a towering breadfruit tree. He tossed down the ripe green fruit. She laughed as she tried to catch the breadfruit, imagining their own child running in the sand, chasing after the tumbling fruit. Maybe, maybe someday.

dugong
large gentle sea animal; manatee

nestled
sheltered as if in a nest

soothing
bringing peace or comfort

33

In the afternoons when the sea crept low, she waded in the tide pools, catching crabs and searching for shells. She stopped to watch as waves washed over the glassy smooth surface, wrinkling the water and sending sparkles of sunshine into the air. It was then that tears would slide down her cheeks. She longed to hold a child in her arms and **caress** it as joyfully as the sun kissed the sea. Maybe, maybe someday.

caress
to touch lovingly

And then it came to be. A child was conceived, began to grow, and soon moved within her.

But she was afraid. As the movements of the child grew stronger, the darkness that chilled her heart grew colder. Her husband laughed at her fears and **chided**: "Follow the ways of the island women. Follow each rule, and our child will be healthy."

chided scolded

"But our child will not be safe."

"Safe from what?"

She did not have an answer.

"Follow each rule." And he turned away from her.

And so she did. In the evenings she no longer went down to the shore to gather crabs and shells and wash off the day's dust. She knew that at dusk the dark spirits are hungry for unborn babies. As darkness thickens, these spirits gather near the water's edge, waiting for foolish young women heavy with growing infants.

She did not eat the foods forbidden to women who are **nourishing** the child within them. Her husband too was careful not to quarrel or hunt fish in the lagoon at night. They both carefully kept the rules of their island.

nourishing
providing food for

The time for birth drew near. The young woman's heart now seemed divided like a half moon. One side glowed warm from the happiness of new life growing strong within her. One half felt dark and cold, heavy with **foreboding** and sadness. About what? Surely just the fear of birthing, the fears that all women share.

She wove new pandanus mats for her child, new mats to make a soft bed. She collected leaves, stripped, soaked, and pounded them. She selected the straightest and softest ones for weaving. Only one more moon cycle to wait. Her time to deliver was a few weeks away, when the moon would be ripening into fullness and light. "Wait, little one, wait. This dark phase of the moon must pass before you are born." She knew that a child born during the moon's darkness was a child filled with evil, doomed to cause **chaos** and destruction. Thus, doomed to die.

chaos
total confusion and disorder

She sang over and over to her child as she wove. "Wait, little one, for the moon to shine, if only a sliver, if only a sliver. Wait, little one, for the brightness needed to assure your life."

But the child would not wait.

That evening, as the blood-red washes of sunset soaked the horizon, her labor pains began.

"No! No!" she cried to her husband. "Run. Find the Old One. Find the woman with herbs that can stop this birthing. Hurry! Run, before it's too late."

Her husband did not answer. Tears clouded his eyes. He looked at the hut's dark opening that showed only the blackness of the night. "The meaning is clear," he said. He turned away.

Her labor quickened. In the darkest hour of the night, the child was born. She cut the cord, washed any uncleanness away, and held her child, saying nothing, knowing that death would come soon. Once the villagers learned that a baby was born during this dark phase of the moon, the baby would be destroyed.

Already she could see that torches were being flamed. A stirring of voices shouting and calling whispered up from the village. She knew the older men were gathering, calling, and encouraging each other. Soon they would come, chanting out words of death, singing **appeasement** to the spirits.

She gazed at her baby. The child looked back at her. His eyes were wide and bright. They seemed to be filled with an understanding that these few minutes were precious.

She caressed his cheek with her hand. His little arms reached up to her. His tiny fist encircled her finger and grasped it tightly. She could feel his strength and eagerness for life.

"No. This child cannot die. There is no darkness, no evil within him."

The chanting of the village men was growing louder, louder.

What could she do? Where could she run?

"Hide us. Hide us!" she pleaded with her husband.

"This island has no place to hide," was his reply.

Her husband was right. There was nowhere to run, no place to hide.

The voices of the men were loud, very loud. The drumming of their words and the slapping of their hands was near, very near.

Nowhere to hide. No way to **plead**.

She clasped her baby tightly to her chest. She stood in front of her home. It was no longer a place of safety. It was no longer her place, her home.

She could already see the angry faces of the men. But their eyes would not look at her. Their feet kept marching and their shouting voices rushed toward her like a wall of sea water about to curl and wash over her and the tiny life she held.

Sea water. Ocean . . . ocean. An enemy, a friend. "I have no friends here. I have no home. I have only the ocean."

She ran. More swiftly than she had ever run before, she fled down the path between the nodding trunks of the coconut palms, nodding, nodding. She raced past hibiscus bushes trembling in the wind, whispering, whispering. She ran faster, faster, until she could feel the knife edges of the volcanic rocks cutting her bare soles. She ran until she could hear the surf crashing against the cliff, just a little farther, a little faster. The men were close behind now, **wailing**, cursing. Hurry, yes, yes. Between gulps of air, she breathed out the words of her own death prayer. "Ocean mother, ocean mother, this child is born of light. No child is born of evil. No child needs to die. No more. No more."

Would the ocean receive them? She must take the chance or the old ways would claim her child's life. In her heart she knew the old ways were wrong. Somehow the ocean would teach her people, a lesson to those still island-bound.

At the cliff's edge she stood holding her baby. She looked down at the swirling waters, the white **froth** of laughing foam. She looked back at the dark faces of her people. She saw their fists shaking at her, their arms reaching, grabbing.

She shouted back. "Never again, not another baby need die!" The young mother leaped.

The men crowded to the edge of the cliff. They looked down but saw no drowning woman or child. Instead they saw the silvery-gray back of an animal they had never seen before, an animal since named

wailing
crying out

froth
bubbles that form in or on liquid

the *dugong*. She was slowly swimming away. Beside her was her infant, splashing and playing in the waves made by its mother.

TURTLE AND CANOE

"I shall prove it *now*." **Eledui** grabbed his hunting spear and pulled it from the **rafters**. "I shall be the best!"

Branches of coconut palms clattered in the night wind. No moon or stars pierced the blackness that wrapped around the island like a warm blindfold. Without hesitation Eledui hurried toward the beach. His feet could see as well as his eyes, sometimes better. Tonight they raced down the stone path to the shore where his outrigger was prepared for the hunt.

The sand was wet. The tide had slipped out, leaving behind wave-rows of shells and coral pieces. Piles of tangled seaweed smelled of yesterday's fish.

Eledui laughed at the ghost crabs that scurried into their dark holes. "Don't worry. Children chase you, not great hunters like me. Tonight I will capture the Great Turtle, the Old One." He thrust his spear and boasted. "For it is I, Eledui from **Ngerdemai**, who hunts with more courage than anyone!"

Quickly Eledui dragged his canoe into the water, leaped aboard, and grabbed the paddle. He glanced back at his village. "The old men waste time waiting for an **omen**. I say, begin the hunt now!"

His fingers gripped the oar's slender throat. "They will see who knows best. The Old One will

Eledui
eh luh THOO ee

rafters
wooden roof
supports

Ngerdemai
ng ur thuh may

omen
object or event
that predicts the
future

fairy tern
small seabird

shuddered
shook, shivered

haste hurry

consent agree

recesses
hidden places

soon be mine!"

He paddled quickly, forgetting to study the horizon for storm swells or look for strong currents. But when a **fairy tern** swooped overhead, shrieking and scolding, he stopped his paddling.

The white bird circled and then dove so close that Eledui could see its black eyes staring at him. He started to laugh but only **shuddered**. The bird had disappeared. Or had he only imagined a bird? Now he remembered. In his hurry, he had forgotten to greet the land spirits, the providers of safety. He had even forgotten to give offerings to the sea spirits. Their powers could protect and assure his safe return or shatter his slender outrigger with a sudden storm. These spirits often changed into birds when traveling to earth with messages or warnings.

Bowing his head, he prayed. "Be pleased, not angered at my boldness. I give thanks for the courage in my bones and the strength in this canoe." He scooped up a handful of salt water and threw it onto the outrigger's bow. "Forgive my **haste**, for my head is filled with thoughts of the hunt." Eledui raised his head and shouted out his prayer. "If the Spirits **consent**, I am ready."

Now he turned and faced the eastern horizon. Already a blood-red line split sea and sky. "I must hurry or I will lose the advantage of the morning sun. Its brightness will blind the turtle's eyes. With the sun behind me, the Old One will see nothing. I can drift closer and closer . . . " Eledui smiled, "and drive my spear through his back!"

With great speed Eledui paddled directly to the outer reef. There he drifted above the sea caves, the Old One's resting place.

The turtle's eyes were dark but clear. He was ancient and preferred the shadowy **recesses** of the coral caves. He rested a long time before the need for air forced him to surface. He needed air now.

A few strokes and the turtle glided upward like a bird winging across the sky. Shafts of morning light beamed through the turquoise water. As soon as his hawk-beak broke the surface, his nostrils flared open. The morning light blinded him. The old one floated with eyes half-closed and breathed in the salty air.

Eledui had been scanning the sea when he saw the mossy domed back of the hawksbill. His heart began pounding. *Yes, there he is! It must be the Old One.* Only one turtle on the reef had a back so big, so wide. *Yes, the Old One, and he shall be mine!*

Before fear could cloud his determination, he pulled his paddle deeply through the water, let the outrigger drift closer and closer until he could see the pattern of squares on the turtle's back. Eledui drew back his spear, aimed, and threw. Blood spurted high into the air. Slowly a circle of red stained the water.

The Old One slid beneath the surface, but the spear's shaft stuck out like a death mark. Eledui dove in and grabbed for the turtle. He must keep the turtle from diving deep below the surface. He must hold onto the shell, kicking to keep the turtle from diving deep into the sea but careful to stay away from his sharp fins. When the Old One grew weak from bleeding and struggling, then he could **lash** it to his outrigger, paddle back, and **strut** triumphantly through his village, holding his trophy high above his head. The children would crowd around pointing and shouting. Young women would stare from a distance. Stories would be told about his great strength and courage and the speed of his paddling.

His paddling . . . where had he dropped his

lash
tie with cord

strut
to walk proudly

paddle? Eledui glanced around him. Where was his boat? In his haste to spear the turtle, Eledui had forgotten to anchor his boat.

He strained to see some sign of his canoe. Now he was the one blinded by the sun's strong light. But yes, he could see its small silhouette already drifting away, caught in the current that ran like a river away from the reef toward the ocean. If he had any hope of catching his boat, he must swim to it now. The ocean was not a place to survive without canoe or paddle.

"Aigh!" The turtle was now quiet, almost as if dead. Eledui shifted his grip. Suddenly the hawksbill twisted and turned, struggling to break free, to dive down, down, down to the safety of a cave.

"I will use the strength of this turtle. I will use his clawing to pull us both toward my boat." Eledui clenched his fists more tightly. His outrigger was his prize possession, but this turtle was his future. He must have both!

The Old One twisted his head, his **gaping** jaw reaching and snapping. But Eledui was quick. The turtle slapped the water with his front fins, trying to tear at Eledui's hands. But the claws could not reach. The turtle rolled onto his back, trying to drown this hunter who had pierced his shell with pain that was burning like fire in every bone, muscle, and even his brain.

Eledui glanced again as his outrigger shrank smaller and smaller, drifting faster and faster away from the reef.

The Old Turtle's fins clawed across Eledui's chest, leaving bloody lines and ripped skin.

"No! I won't give up. I won't let go and return empty-handed. Never!" He swam harder, pushing the Old One in front of him away from the reef,

gaping
wide open

toward the sea and drifting canoe. Waves splashed, choking him with water and salt. His eyes burned. The strength in his arms was nearly gone. No longer were his muscles powerful and strong. The weight of the Old One felt heavier and heavier. When he stared at the horizon, sometimes he saw the tiny **silhouette** of his outrigger but sometimes all he saw was the black tip of a distant wave.

silhouette
outline

The turtle lifted his head and sucked in a long breath of air. And then the Old One dipped his head under the surface and pushed hard with front fins and back. He would dive to the deepest cave even if he must take this hunter with him.

Eledui now saw the sadness in the turtle's eyes and felt a shudder of death and sorrow. Around both hunter and turtle, the sea foamed red with blood. Eledui felt the shell's sharp edge slide from his fists. He lunged for the turtle but the Old One slipped beneath the sea.

"No! No!" he screamed. But the only ones to hear his cries were the waves and the empty horizon.

LA KAKELOK (MAN MAKE FLY)

On the small island of **Ebon**, a woman must never be left alone after having her first child. If a new mother is left alone, she might turn into a **Mejenkwaad**. A Mejenkwaad is a witch. A witch who eats people.

One time on Ebon, a man and his wife were happily married. After a time, the woman became pregnant. Following the time of many tides a little son was born. This family of three was so happy!

The man fished and gathered food for his wife and son. The wife nursed their baby. The man was careful and never, not even once, left his wife alone. He knew about Mejenkwaad.

As their son approached his first birthday, his parents wished to have a celebration. Much food was needed. Everyone living on Ebon (which was not very big) was invited.

"My husband," the wife announced, "we need still more food. There is not enough taro or bread-fruit on our whole island. Can you go to Bikini, and to **Jaluit**, and bring back more?"

The husband was uneasy at leaving, but he knew they needed more food. "I will go," he answered, "but you must stay with others to keep away the Mejenkwaad."

"Do not worry," the young wife laughed. "It is

La Kakelok
  la ka keh lock

Ebon eh bun

Mejenkwaad
  meh jehnk wad

Jaluit
JAL uh wuht

45

already one year since our son's birth. I will be safe. You may take our son with you on his first canoe adventure!"

The boy and his father sailed for Jaluit. Of course, as soon as the boat was out of sight, the foolish wife turned into a Mejenkwaad. Soon she began to eat all the rest of the islanders.

By the time the man and his son returned, all of the islanders had been **devoured** by the hungry Mejenkwaad. The man left his crew by the boat, and walked with his son to the strangely quiet village. There he was met by the Mejenkwaad, disguised as his wife.

devoured
eaten greedily

"Welcome home, husband," the Mejenkwaad hissed. "I am SO happy to see you and this nice fat son of ours." (The little boy looked very plump and tasty to the Mejenkwaad.)

"But where is everyone else?" asked the husband.

The Mejenkwaad gave a clever answer. "They are all down at the beach on the other side of the island. There has been a huge tuna catch. Let us hurry and join them before all the fish are gone! You go first, my husband. I will be right behind you."

"Let's go," answered the husband. "I will carry our son. You go first."

"No," insisted the Mejenkwaad. "You go first." She wanted to sneak up behind and eat them both!

The husband was puzzled at his wife's strange behavior. He was also puzzled that the village was so very empty. It did not look as though anyone had been there for many days.

The little boy began to cry. "Quiet, my son," soothed the father. "Why," he wondered, "does my wife not come to comfort her son?"

To calm the crying boy, the father quickly made a small toy from the leaf of a coconut tree. This toy made a gentle whirring noise when the breeze blew. The little boy fell asleep in his father's arms.

"Now hurry," **goaded** the Mejenkwaad. "The fish will be all gone." They hurried down the path, first the man and his son. Close behind them followed the Mejenkwaad. The path led into a dark forest, but a breeze from behind them kept the small toy whirring. The boy slept on.

As the path became darker, the Mejenkwaad crept closer and closer. Soon she was right behind the man. She reached out her long arms. She was so close that her body blocked the forest breeze. The little toy stopped whirring.

"Waaa," cried the boy. The man turned around to see why the wind had stopped. He was surprised to find his "wife" so close behind.

"You are too close, wife. You must give the breeze space to blow the toy." The Mejenkwaad moved back, and the toy whirred again. The little boy went back to sleep.

Now the path was even darker. This time the Mejenkwaad decided to rush up quickly and grab the pair before the boy awoke. As she dashed forward her body again blocked the breeze and the toy became silent.

"What is the matter this time?" wondered the father. He turned around quickly and the Mejenkwaad almost ran right into him!

Now the father understood what was happening. "Alas, my good wife is gone," he thought. "Now my son and I are in danger as well."

The father thought quickly. "I must **relieve myself** in the forest," he told the Mejenkwaad. "My son and I will be right back."

"All right, my dear," answered the Mejenkwaad. "But hurry or the fish will be gone."

Once hidden in the dark forest, the clever father found some palm leaves and made a new toy. This toy caught the breeze and made a sound, "rub-rub-rub." This sounded just like a person having gas. He put the toy high in a tree to catch the wind. Then he took his son and ran away into the forest.

"Rub-rub-rub," went the little toy. "My, that man has a lot of gas," thought the Mejenkwaad.

After quite a long wait, the "rub-rub-rub" sound was still loud. Mejenkwaad was tired of waiting. She held her nose and rushed into the forest. "I've got you now," she shouted as she grabbed at the sound. But all she grabbed was the little palm-leaf toy. She was SO mad that she ate the toy!

Meanwhile, the man and his son ran to the far side of the island. A large pile of empty coconut shells lay there. The father picked up a shell and carved yet another toy. This one made a loud "Whooo." It sounded like a man calling for help.

He ran to the east shore of the island and put one of these toys high in the trees. Then he ran and put another on the west shore. He put yet another on the shore to the south.

Finally, he ran to his boat, on the north side of the island, and set off to sea with his son and his crew. "Hurry! I have a plan to get rid of this witch, but we must be far away before she finds us."

The Mejenkwaad was confused. She could hear the man calling "Whooo" from all over the little island. First she ran to the east, but found only the coconut-shell toy. The same thing happened when she rushed back to the west. It happened again when she ran to the south. She ate all of the shells and tried to think.

"The north!" she thought. "He must have run and hidden in the north." She ran to the north. The

Mejenkwaad searched all the huts in the village. All she found were bones, the bones of all the villagers she had eaten. They were dry and tasteless. There was not a bit of meat left. All the Mejenkwaad could think about was that plump and tasty little baby. Then she realized the canoe was gone. The man had escaped!

Because the Mejenkwaad was a witch, she had special powers. She stretched up her neck longer and longer until her head was taller than the tallest coconut palm. She no longer looked like a woman. Now she had a horrible head and a huge hungry mouth. From above the palms she could see far out into the **lagoon**. She saw the little canoe sailing close to Jaluit.

"I've got them now!" she cried. The Mejenkwaad stretched her neck out longer and longer. Then she flung out her horrible head to swallow the canoe.

The men in the canoe saw the giant head and were terrified. But the father had a plan. "Don't be afraid. Follow my instructions exactly. When I cry out, 'Turn to the left,' you must instead turn the canoe sharply to the right."

The men were so frightened that they agreed at once. When the horrible head was almost upon them the father shouted, "Turn left!" The men, as instructed, turned the boat to the right. The Mejenkwaad, hearing the cry "Turn left," turned at the last minute to the left. She missed the boat and bit down on a large mouthful of ocean water. She came up sputtering with rage.

The Mejenkwaad drew back for another try.

"This time," the father instructed, "when I say, 'Turn right,' you must instead turn the canoe to the left."

Once again the Mejenkwaad struck out. When all

lagoon
shallow body of water, often surrounded by a reef or an atoll

49

appeared to be lost, the father cried out, "Turn right!" The boat of course turned to the left, but the Mejenkwaad, thinking the boat would go right, struck that way. Again, all she got was a mouthful of sea water.

By this time, the canoe had arrived in the region of Jaluit at a place called Anwar. Here there is a deep **crevice** in the reef. Many large fish hide in this place. The men quickly set anchor and waited.

crevice
narrow opening or crack

Once again the father made a toy. This time it was a small glider made from the leaf of a pandanus tree. When the Mejenkwaad struck this time, he threw the glider into the air. The Mejenkwaad could not resist this little tidbit. At the last minute she veered off course to snatch the little toy. Her head crashed into the ocean, sending fountains of water into the air.

Beneath the surface of the lagoon, in the crevice at Anwar, lived a giant shark. "Who is disturbing my lagoon?" thought the shark. He looked up and saw the witch's head still in his lagoon water chewing the toy glider. He was so mad! The shark swam right up to that Mejenkwaad, opened his giant mouth, and swallowed the whole Mejenkwaad in a single bite.

That was the end of that Mejenkwaad. Even to this day, in the ocean near Jaluit, at Anwar, there is a deep crevice in the reef. Sharks of great size and even greater appetites live there. They swim around, waiting. Perhaps they are waiting for another tasty meal of Mejenkwaad.

HOW TO STEAL THE MOON

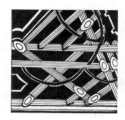

Long ago, the chief of a tiny atoll in the Central Caroline Islands had a beautiful daughter. She was so beautiful she refused to marry the young men of her island. Her father worried about her, especially at night, when he would gaze at the moon. He loved the moon. Then he had an idea: he would gather the people of the island together and find someone clever enough to bring it down from the sky. Such a person would be worthy of his daughter.

At the chief's meeting, a boy appeared. He claimed he could deliver to his chief the glowing white moon. He was from a poor family, but the chief didn't mind. "Give it your best try," he told him. So the boy went home to ask his mother's advice.

"There is a path that leads to the moon," his mother said. "It's invisible except to those who are walking on it. One end reaches to the beach where the bent palm tree grows. Go there and reach up with your arms. Like this." His mother stood as tall as she could and reached into the sky. "A power like the wind will lift you up. Then the path will grow solid under your feet. It glitters like golden **flecks** in the sand. Follow the path all the way to the moon."

The boy did as his mother instructed. He walked all the way up to the moon. On the way, he passed

flecks
spots, flakes, small particles

plovers
shore birds with
short bills

taboo
forbidden, off-
limits, not
allowed

Yalulep
yah loo lep

ridgepole
highest horizon-
tal timber of a
roof

several people sitting by the edge of the path. They gave him many gifts: two **plovers**, two roosters, one pandanus fruit, and a hibiscus stick.

When he reached heaven, the boy entered a men's house that was **taboo** for humans. Inside sat **Yalulep**, the Carolinian high god. And there, hanging from the **ridgepole**, was the moon! The moon belonged to Yalulep. How could the boy get it away from him?

He began to tell stories to Yalulep's guards, who were sitting outside the meeting house. They were beautiful, sweet stories. One by one the guards fell asleep. Then the boy sneaked back inside Yalulep's house and untied the moon. He hid its bright side against his body so no light would spill. Then he crept back outside as quietly as he could. When he was far enough away, he ran as fast as he could back to earth!

Yalulep yelled with rage when he discovered he had been robbed. He sent a fast runner to chase after the boy. Fast, fast, they ran, wind whistling in their ears. The runner was faster than the boy. Just as he lunged for the boy's heels, the boy untied the two plovers he had been given on the walk up to the sky. Right away they began to fight! The runner couldn't help it—he sat down to watch. The boy ran on.

The runner soon realized the boy was escaping, so he got up and chased him. Soon he was so close the boy could feel his hot breath on his neck! Then the boy untied the roosters and let them go. They began to peck each other's eyes out. The runner couldn't help it—this he had to see. He decided to take the roosters for himself. He wrapped his hands around the roosters' throats and ran back to heaven.

Yalulep was angry. "You greedy rooster-grabber!" he yelled. He called his fastest runner of all, who ran as fast as the wind. "Catch that boy who stole my moon," he yelled. How fast the fastest runner caught the boy! The boy felt his hand tighten around his ankle. Just as he began to fall, the boy threw down the pandanus fruit. A huge jungle of pandanus sprang up, thick as the stars in the heavens! The boy was on one side of this spiny jungle, and the runner was on the other. Yalulep's runner didn't have a **machete**. He could barely crawl through the thick, spiky plants. Soon his hands and feet were covered with blood.

machete
large, heavy knife

The boy was nearly back on earth. Oh no! The fastest runner came out of the pandanus jungle and grabbed him by the hair! The boy threw down the hibiscus stick. Again a jungle sprang up. This time the boy made it safely home. His mother welcomed him with delicious fish and breadfruit.

The boy went to the chief's house. Proudly, he handed him the glowing **sphere**. But he warned the chief that he must follow his mother's words exactly. "Do not take the covers off the moon," he said.

sphere
ball, globe

The chief considered these words and nodded. "Now you have earned my blessing to marry my daughter," the chief said.

Alas, the chief could not resist his curiosity. What could be so wrong with peeling off just one layer of the glowing moon? So one day he peeled back the thinnest outer layer of the moon. It grew brighter and more beautiful, like the golden inside of a mango. So he peeled off another. And another. What was wrong with brightness? What was wrong with beauty? Uh oh—the chief took off all of the covers.

The moon slipped from his hands, as slippery as a fish. The bright, beautiful moon, the dazzling moon, flew off to its home in the sky. The chief was very sad about this. He called the boy to ask for advice. "There's nothing I can do," said the boy. "It is better this way. Now everyone who looks up will know that this moon belongs to you." The chief nodded. He hadn't thought of it that way.

After that, the chief was happy. He watched his moon each night, like a glowing ring in the ear of the sky.

K'OW AND BUNENEY

In a time long ago, the people of Yap could change their form. They could become an animal, or even a plant, if they wished.

One **vain** young woman decided to become a Buneney, an elegant white crane.

The Buneney was beautiful, with glistening white feathers and a graceful long neck. She used her long neck often, especially to look at her reflection in the still pools of water near the lagoon.

"My, I am truly beautiful!" she would announce. "I deserve to marry a handsome man."

Day after day, Buneney spent her mornings looking at herself in her water mirror. She did not notice the shy gray crane, K'ow, who watched her from beneath the coconut palms.

Many young men of the village wished to marry the beautiful Buneney. She refused them all. "You men of this village are too plain for me. I must marry an especially elegant man."

One by one the men went away, muttering about the proud Buneney. But K'ow continued to watch. Every day he brought her gifts of fish and fresh food. She never once said, "Thank you." In fact, she did not even seem to notice K'ow.

One day **Molob**, the great black frigate bird, came to this village on Yap. He had heard of the beautiful

K'ow   koh
Buneney
   boo neh nee

vain
   foolish;
   impressed with
   one's own
   appearance

Molob   moh lohb

55

Buneney. He wished to see her for himself. Now Molob was a large and handsome bird. His kind is rarely seen near the land. He prefers to soar far above the ocean, almost in the clouds themselves.

Buneney was beside herself. Molob was so handsome! Molob was so big. And Molob had asked Buneney to be his wife.

"Oh, yes!" Buneney replied. "I will **soar** with you. We can look down on these lowly villagers together."

Buneney was a land crane, so she could not fly high. Molob was very large and very strong. He placed Buneney on his broad back. Together they soared high into the sky.

Far below, little K'ow wiped the tears from his eyes. He went back to gathering fish and food for his supper. He missed the white crane. He loved her and did not even mind that she never spoke to him. Now she was gone.

Molob and Buneney flew higher than Buneney had ever imagined. The land below looked like a toy. She could hardly see the people at all. "This is the life, Molob. Yes, this is the life!"

After a time, Buneney was beginning to feel a little tired. "Molob," she asked, "Where is our home to be?"

"This is our home," replied Molob. "I live here in the sky. Do you like your new home?"

"Well," answered Buneney, "I think so. But I do miss my nest on the ground a little bit."

Later, as they flew higher and higher, Buneney found herself feeling a bit hungry. On the ground, when she felt hungry she just opened her mouth. That nice gray crane, K'ow, was always right there to pop in a fresh fish. Maybe Molob would be nice too?

soar
fly or glide high
in the air

"Molob, my husband."

"Yes, Buneney?"

"What is there to eat, in this magnificent home in the sky?"

"Eat? Why just open your mouth, my wife, and fly to the east."

Buneney opened her mouth and flew toward the east. Nothing happened.

"I am still hungry," she said.

"Open your mouth and fly toward the west this time."

She did, but still nothing happened. She was getting very hungry.

"Husband, I am VERY hungry, and I cannot find anything to eat."

"But Buneney," Molob answered, "I eat only the air. Isn't it delicious?"

"But Molob," Buneney wailed, "I eat fish and taro. I cannot eat your air."

"I am sorry, Buneney. These foods are strange to me. I do not have any of them here."

"Then please," Buneney begged, "take me back to the earth before I am too weak and die."

Molob the frigate bird took Buneney back to the earth. He put her down on a beach not far from her home. Then he launched himself back into the air and was gone.

Buneney was so weak she could hardly move. Nearby she saw a small fish trap. There were some fish caught in the trap. She did not see K'ow, the owner of the trap, sitting nearby on a rock. She took a fish.

"Who is stealing my fish?" K'ow demanded, pretending not to see Buneney.

"Oh please," begged Buneney, "I am starving. Please let me have a little food."

"All right," answered K'ow. "Since you are hungry I will give you coconut to drink and fish to eat." He also gave her taro to eat and betel nut to chew.

Buneney ate. She looked **gratefully** at the gray crane. How kind he was. How strong he looked as he gathered the fish and brought her taro.

gratefully
thankfully

"K'ow, I am sorry I was so mean to you. I see you are a good provider. You have a caring heart. I would like to marry you if you will still have me."

K'ow was overjoyed. "Remember," he counseled, "The wind does not always blow from the same direction." Which is to say that one should think twice before leaping. Buneney knew this now. She had leaped far into the air and had almost died. Now she would stay on the ground.

K'ow and Buneney lived happily together for many years. They had many children. And Buneney always had plenty to eat.

THE ISLAND OF THE DOLPHIN GIRLS

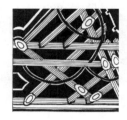

There was once a chief's son named **Anoun Farrang**. He was of the **Lugenfanu** clan, from Farrang, near Chuuk. He liked to sail with adult men from Losap to Chuuk. The ends of the sailing canoe were beautiful, like swans' necks reaching up toward the sky. The navigator was teaching him how to steer the canoe. Soon he would know enough and would become a man like them. He was practicing with the **tiller** when a group of playful dolphins swam up to the canoe.

Ah, but they only appeared to be dolphins—they were really girls! They were quite taken with the chief's son. "He's so handsome," they cried to one another. One very bold girl swam straight at the canoe. She leaped up, **lashed** her strong, gray tail, and knocked the boy overboard! The men didn't hear the splash or see the brown legs of the boy disappear into the dark blue water. And because the sea was gentle that day, they didn't even notice that no one was steering the canoe.

The boy wasn't frightened. He said a chant to ask his magic powers to show him which direction to swim—north, south, east, or west. But his magic powers didn't answer. Then he said the chant again. His magic told him to dive straight down into the sea.

Anoun Farrang
ah noon fahr rahng

Lugenfanu
loo gehn fah noo

tiller
the part of the boat used for steering

lashed
moved suddenly or violently

Down, down he swam. Finally he came to a **lush** island covered with shady trees and flowers of every color. In the middle of the island was a large pool—clean and deep and inviting! The boy hid in the bushes to see if the pool belonged to anyone. For a long time he waited. Then the dolphins came. They dove from the salt water of the ocean into the clear fresh water of the pool. The boy stayed hidden in the bushes, watching. A dolphin climbed out of the pool and began taking off her skin. She turned into a beautiful girl. Then all the other dolphins did the same. They threw their skins into a big pile.

The boy was full of mischief. When the girls were splashing and laughing, he grabbed a skin. He made sure to grab the skin of the prettiest girl. Later, the girls put their skins back on and once again were dolphins. The prettiest girl looked everywhere but could not find her skin. She ran around and around, looking under every rock, looking up into the trees. She ran her hands down her girl's body over and over as if her precious skin were there. Finally, the other dolphins swam back into the ocean. The poor girl was left all alone.

The boy came out from where he had been hiding in the tall grass. "What's the matter?" he asked her.

"I lost my skin," she said. Tears spilled down her rosy cheeks.

At this, the boy felt such pity he gave her her skin back. "Why did you do that?" she cried. "Why did you take it?"

"Because I wanted to talk to you," he said. He was sorry and not sorry.

"Oh," she said, staring at him. "Where did you come from?"

The boy told her about the voyage from Losap to Chuuk. He told how the dolphins had swum by and how one of them had knocked him out of the canoe. And how he had found the undersea island and the pool and the prettiest dolphin-girl.

"Oh dear," she said. "I knocked you out of the canoe! I guess I'm like you—I wanted to make sure I could talk to you." They looked at each other and laughed.

The girl invited the boy to visit her house. While they were there, they heard the dolphins dive into the freshwater pool. "Uh oh," the girl said. "They'll come here next. Quick, I'll hide you!" She hid the boy under a pile of woven mats. Soon the girls arrived. "So there you are," they said. "We've been looking all over for you."

Another girl said, "It smells funny here. Like a human."

The prettiest girl laughed. "Oh, you're just smelling me. I smell funny because I've been stuck on land all day."

"No," said the other girls. "It's not you. You're trying to trick us. Tell us who's here!"

They wouldn't stop asking questions. Finally, the prettiest girl said, "Well then, what IF someone is here? What are you going to do?"

"We'll be nice," said one.

"We'll marry him," said another.

"We'll take him swimming every day," said a third.

"All right. He's under the mats." The group of girls tore off the mats and found the boy.

"He's so handsome!" they cried out. "Where did you find him?"

"What a good friend to have," said one.

"Such a handsome husband," said another.

"Let's take him swimming!" suggested the third.

They decided that the boy should stay in the

house and someone should stay with him. The others would gather food. They liked to eat fresh, delicious fruits and vegetables—taro, pineapple, coconut, papaya—but they didn't know how to cook. They ate everything raw. The boy rubbed sticks together until a spark appeared. Using twigs and dried leaves, he lit a fire. Then he roasted every food and made special mixtures—roasted coconut and mashed banana. He taught them how much better food tasted after it was cooked. This made them even happier they had found him.

Many days went by. When the prettiest girl came again to stay with the boy, he said, "I want to go home. I miss my parents and my island."

When the other girls heard this, they cried many salty tears. "We want you to live here with us."

"I'm sorry. I need to go. My family is worrying about me. They must think I'm dead. I will try to come back here, but you must let me go home."

They held a farewell feast for the boy. He taught them some medicine especially for dolphins, using plants found near their bathing place. They would know how to cure themselves if they got sick. Then they built a special cage and piled their best foods inside. The boy climbed in and sat among the bread-fruits and watermelons, loquats and mangos. How sweet and delicious it smelled! The dolphins lifted the cage onto their backs. Moving their tails up and down, up and down, they pushed the cage upward through the sea. They swam all the way back to Losap with the boy inside the cage.

When they entered Losap's lagoon, the people on that atoll cried, "Look! A great canoe is coming!" The dolphins pushed the cage closer and closer. Finally, the people could see that the canoe was actually a cage. When they saw the chief's son inside, they yelled with joy. The people of Losap were happy that day. Gladly they accepted the gifts from the dolphin-girls, especially the gift of a human life.

TIK AND LAP AND THE RAVENOUS FISH

Tik teek

Lap lahp

Ninuau
nee noo ow

ravenous
very hungry

pleaded begged

bosom breasts

Long before ships began to bring food to the people of Pohnpei, a woman had twin boys, **Ninuau** Tik and Ninuau Lap. Like many children on this blessed island, Tik and Lap knew how to make magic. They were good at fishing with spears they made out of long, sharpened sticks. Their mother was proud of them. She was also afraid because Tik and Lap were so sure of themselves they weren't careful. They were fearless.

"Don't dive so deep," she **pleaded**. Their heads didn't yet rise above her shoulder. "Your foot could get caught in the reef."

"We are great swimmers, mother, better than the older men!" Lap boasted.

"We take care of each other. Don't worry," said Tik.

"You boys think the ocean is like a mother. She is salty and warm and holds you in her **bosom**. But you are wrong. She is also strong and powerful. Some day she will pull you out to sea."

Tik and Lap didn't believe her. They loved the water as much as they loved the air. They knew themselves to be very strong and clever. They grew tired of staying in the shallow lagoon. Surely such good fishermen deserved a sailing canoe.

The more their mother told them to be careful,

the farther away the boys swam. They were always looking for a new adventure.

"Did you see that black-tipped shark?" Tik said.

"Yes," said Lap. "Let's chase it."

Together they beat the water with their spears until they scared the shark away. Then they stood on the sandy bottom and laughed. They felt more powerful than all the creatures of the sea.

One day they visited a **submerged** reef in front of the island of **Samuin**. A thin **coil** of black smoke rose from among the island's trees.

"Oh, it smells so good. Surely they will offer us food," said Tik.

"I am very hungry," said Lap. "Let's swim for it."

They crawled up onto the shore. A huge crowd of people was preparing a feast for their chief. When the people saw the young boys from Pohnpei, they invited them to eat. The chief was so delighted with the stories the boys told that he gave them a lot of food. It was so much food he had to give them a canoe to carry it all!

"What is all this?" their mother asked when they showed her the crabs and coconuts and ripe sweet bananas and steamed taro and breadfruit. It was enough food to feed their family for a long time.

"All this comes from the chief of Samuin Island," they said.

"He liked us so much he gave it to us," said Tik. He was as proud as if he had grown it all himself.

"Gifts must be exchanged for gifts, my sons," said their mother, looking more worried than ever. "You must both go before dawn tomorrow and catch the biggest, best fish you can. You may use your new canoe. But please, please, take care of yourselves."

"Mother, you have no idea—we swim like tunas,

submerged
underwater

Samuin
    sah moo een

coil
    spiral; series of
    connected loops

petrels
   small, long-
    winged seabirds

dive like **petrels**, and sail as fast as the south wind. You will see," said Lap, winking at Tik.

The boys went out the next morning while the starlight was pulsing in the heavens. When they were hungry, they stopped at a tiny island. They had brought a large coconut to eat and drink. Tik knelt on the rocky shore of the island to make a fire. Lap cracked their coconut in two. The milk ran over his hands and made them slippery. The largest part of the coconut suddenly slipped from his hands. It fell into the deep blue-black water where they had tied their canoe.

There was no time to think! The boys dove into the dark water. Down, down they went, chasing the sinking coconut deeper and deeper. They knew better than to dive without looking first, but neither wanted to go hungry. They did not know that a giant fish lived below these rocks. He saw the tiny coconut go by and two swimming bodies chasing it.

Suddenly he opened his mouth wide! Tik and Lap saw a ring of sharp white teeth. Then the world turned black. Down, down inside the belly of the giant fish they slid, his slimy warm **membrane** slipping along their backs. They screamed, but the sound was muffled. It was as if they were inside a sealed cave with no air hole. Not even a glimmer of light.

membrane
   thin layer (in
   this case, of the
   stomach lining)

"We're in its horrible stomach. It smells like rotting fish guts," said Tik.

"I don't want to die in this horrible place," his brother said. "We must make a fire. Look, you're still holding the firewood!"

Tik began to rub the pieces of wood together as fast as he could. He was expert at making fires, but the wood had gotten wet. They blew on it and rubbed and rubbed until a spark appeared. A tongue of flame began to lick the wood. Tik used the stick as a torch. "This place is so ugly and slimy. We've got to get out of here."

"Of course! But first we're going to roast this fish!"

They held the wood against the fish's stomach wall. The fish began to **writhe** in pain.

writhe to twist

"Get ready for a wild ride!" warned Lap. The fish went crazy, throwing itself against the undersea rocks. It dragged its belly against the coral reef. Then the fish flipped over and over in the water to try to get rid of the terrible burning pain. Finally it swam straight out to sea and dove to the bottom. It **lashed** its massive tail once more and died.

lashed moved suddenly or violently

Tik and Lap had clung to the inside of the fish's stomach. They hung near the sharp gills below its mouth. They weren't burned, but their hair was **singed** and their skin was black with smoke. Their hands bled, but they didn't mind. They were glad to be alive. Slowly they felt the fish rising. Then they heard the gentle slap-slapping of the ocean swells.

singed lightly burned

"Let's get out of here," said Tik. They crawled out of the dead fish's mouth. There was Samuin Island, a thin green line on the horizon. They pushed and pulled the fish all the way to the island. They crawled up onto shore in front of the amazed islanders. Tik said, "We have brought a gift for your chief."

The chief was pleased. "How could such small boys catch such a huge fish?" he asked. "Did you use magic?"

"We just used ourselves. We were the bait for the fish!" **crowed** Tik.

crowed bragged

"He swallowed us whole and then we roasted him from the inside!" added Lap proudly.

"You are clever boys," said the chief. "Pay

attention to your elders—especially your mother—and you will grow up to be wise men."

Tik and Lap sailed home under the hot afternoon sun. They told their mother everything that had happened. How dark and slimy it was inside the fish. How they had given the best gift ever to the chief of Samuin.

"I am proud that you have repaid his gift," their mother said. "But I'm not glad that you were nearly killed."

"We forgot to look before we dove," Tik mumbled. His eyes were cast down on his bare feet.

"We were careless," Lap said.

"And from that you have gained wisdom," their mother answered. She looked into the deep brown eyes of each of her sons. "You are now becoming real men."

HINA AND THE WOODEN BIRD

The rain began to sprinkle, tap-tapping on the leaves and the sand. The youngest child of the rain god was learning how to water the land. "Good!" said the rain god. "Now you next," it urged the next oldest child. And the rain falling from the sky onto Kapingamarangi Atoll in the eastern Caroline Islands became a little heavier.

Down below the clouds, a young girl named Hina lived with her brother **Ruapongongo**. Hina was in charge of airing out her family's sleeping mats. She had been born with only one leg, but she managed to do her work just fine. One by one she dragged the mats outside. Ruapongongo helped her lay them flat in the sun. Their parents were gone for the day. Hina and her brother went back inside their warm **thatch** house and fell asleep. Hina slept and slept. Even when the rain began to tap-tap upon the roof, she kept sleeping. In her dream, she was swimming among shiny blue fish with golden fins.

Up in the sky, the rain god called to his children. "None of you has awakened the young girl. She is supposed to care for her family's mats. You, my oldest, make rain that beats so hard her ears shout, 'Wake up!'" And so the oldest rain child poured rain.

Down below, **rivulets** of water ran between the

Kapingamarangi
kah peeng ah mah RAHNG ee

Hina   HEE nah

Ruapongongo
roo ah pahng AHNG oh

thatch
straw or grass used as a house covering

rivulets
small streams

trees. Rain thumped on the roof and splashed on the mats. Still, Hina did not wake up.

Finally, the rain god himself rained the rain of all rains. Birds took cover to protect the **glistening** oils on their feathers. Crabs **skittered** far into the jungle. At last, Hina and Ruapongongo woke up. Hina heard the rain and ran outside on her one leg as fast as she could. She grabbed the mats, but many had already been swept away.

At last the rain of all rains stopped. The sky grew soft and gray again. Then it split open to reveal the gleaming face of the sun. Hina was afraid. Her parents came home and their faces were full of anger. Her mother was holding one of the mats, the one that held the family's special sharks' teeth. But now it was empty.

Her father said, "You are a worthless girl. Go search until you find everything you have lost. Go now!"

Hina wept, but she knew she had no choice but to make this journey. She waded out into the lagoon. Soon she was floating in the gentle surf. A shark swam past her, singing a shark song. "Have you come to take me with you?" she called out.

The shark said, "Oh no, I am just trying to remember the chant my father taught me. Goodbye."

A small fish brushed against Hina's foot. "Are you the one who has come for me?" Hina asked.

"Can't you see I'm much too small?" said the fish. "Besides, I'm just swimming along."

A parrot fish passed by next, but it had the same answer for Hina. They were all busy singing their own songs.

Hina was so discouraged she began to cry. A large sea turtle swam past. "Are you the one who has come for me?" she said.

glistening
shining

skittered
moved lightly or quickly

"Yes, I'm the one. You must climb on my back and hold on no matter what." Hina climbed onto the turtle's hard back. She wrapped her two small hands around the top edge of his giant shell. They swam and swam into the open sea.

"**Nuuuuu**!" Hina cried, when her home island was far out of sight. "I am so thirsty."

The turtle replied, "Don't cry. Take the coconut nearest to your hand. Husk it with your teeth. Then I will crack it open for you so you can drink the sweet milk."

Hina did as she was told—almost. Instead of letting the turtle crack the coconut, she smashed it against his head. The turtle was so angry he flipped Hina off into the water. He dove down, down into the dark blue. Hina swam, calling and calling for the turtle to come back to her. Her leg and arms grew so heavy they felt like stones. "I am lost," she thought. "And all because I slept through the rain."

Just as she let her head slip under water, the turtle's strong back rose from the dark world beneath. He caught her perfectly. "You know it is **taboo** to touch my head!" the turtle hissed. "Do not ever do that again." The turtle was angry, but he was an old soul, and through his long life he had developed a special **fondness** for the young. Even for human young.

They swam in silence for a long time. Hina's voice was small and weak, but the turtle heard her quietly whisper, "Nuuuuu! I see land!"

"No, no, that is not land. That's a **parua-tanamoana**, an angry sea demon. You must hide!" The turtle shook violently, causing Hina to slip off into the water. She held on by one hand. When the sea demon came still closer, she let go, took a huge gulp of air, and let herself slide down under the

nuuuuu
noo (with the oo long and drawn out)

taboo
forbidden, not allowed

fondness
liking, affection

parua-tanamoana
pah ROO ah tah nah moh AH nah

71

turtle's body.

"I smell human!" shouted the demon.

"But I am a turtle, nothing more. And I am just swimming along," said the turtle.

"Turn your belly up to me!" commanded the demon.

Hina rose for air on the far side of the turtle. The demon could not see her.

"Now turn so I can see your back!" Again, Hina hid. When she came up again, the demon was gone.

She and the turtle swam on. A long time passed. Then she groaned her small, sad groan. "Nuuuuu!"

"Those are the islands known as **Tinirau**," the turtle answered. "We will go there. I am tired. You must fetch fresh green banana leaves for me to rest on." Hina did as she was told. While the turtle was resting in the shade, she explored the island. Unlucky girl! The first house she came to belonged to a magician. It was taboo to enter it. She went inside anyway, without even asking permission. "Look," the people said, "a strange girl with one leg!"

"You belong to us now," said the magician. He made her a tiny house out of leaves. "You can eat only grass and ashes from the fire. Do not complain or you'll be very, very sorry!"

Hina was a **captive** for a very long time. The turtle eventually swam away. Finally, her brother Ruapongongo set out to find her. With his stone axe and his best shell knife, he carved a flying bird out of a tree. He painted it with soot and oil to look like a huge **petrel**. He flew over many islands looking for his sister. At long last, he saw a strange island sticking up out of the sea like the fist of a drowning man. There he saw Hina.

He landed the bird beside the magician's house.

The magician was hiding inside, watching. "Aha!" he cried, running outside. "Now I have a huge bird to take me places." Immediately he began worrying about how he would feed such a large bird. He didn't want it to go away—he would tame it and use it to make bad magic. "Oh handsome bird, do you like tuna?" he asked.

Ruapongongo was hiding inside, trying not to laugh out loud. "Yes," he answered.

The magician ordered everyone into their canoes to catch tunas for the bird. As soon as they had all gone, Ruapongongo called out, "Pssst, Hina! It's your brother. I have come to take you home!" Hina climbed into the bird. She wept to be going home at last.

"Fly!" she said. "Fly far away from here!"

"But first I want to play a trick on that bad magician," said Ruapongongo. He made the bird fly low over the fishing canoes. The magician believed the bird must be very hungry. "Hurry up! You are so slow!" he said to his people. "Throw him a tuna!" he ordered. The people threw their newly caught tunas into the air. The bird caught them all!

"Hina," whispered Ruapongongo. "Now let's show the magician that he has been outsmarted. Let your leg hang over the side. He will know it is you."

Hina did not like this game, but she let her leg hang over the side. "The bird has stolen your servant girl!" the people cried. Secretly, they were pleased. They did not like the evil magician either.

The magician was so upset he lost some of his magic powers that day. His curses and chants made no sense. The people were free again to do as they liked. The wooden bird flew Hina and Ruapongongo back home to **Touhou** Island in Kapingamarangi Atoll. But Ruapongongo wasn't satisfied yet. He

Touhou
toh oo hoh

73

flew back again to the strange island. In the jungle, he built the magician a tiny leaf house to live in. Then he tricked him into coming inside and he locked him up! Now the evil magician would know how Hina had felt. Ruapongongo forced the magician to eat leaves and ash. Then he flew home again.

That's all there is to tell, just a tale told by the people.

STRONG OLD MAGIC

AS TOLD BY LATIK JOHN

"**T**he old magic is not used anymore. On my island, Kapingamarangi, the people threw away the strong magic when the church people came. They threw away their dances and their story talk. Throw-away, throw-away! And they stopped using the old magic, **mokopuna**."

Latik was busy weaving flowers into a head wreath, a **mwaar**. She was helping her friend make the thirty-nine flower wreaths needed for the Catholic confirmation celebration. They had stayed up most of the night weaving flowers into colorful crowns. The tiny room where she sat and wove was filled with blossoms. An old tin pail was filled with creamy plumeria. Piles of bougainvillea blooms tumbled across the floor—**fuchsia**, pink, red, purple, even orange. Heaps of green vines had been stacked by her side. The room looked as if someone were about to weave a rainbow.

"You might be afraid if you come to my island." Latik laughed. " I think that when you go there, you will be plenty scared." Latik's face was round like a coconut and the same handsome brown. When she laughed, her eyes sparkled with amusement.

"Why will I be scared?" Shivers tingled down my back. I was remembering her words about the strong old magic.

Kapingamarangi
kah peeng ah mah
RAHNG ee

Latik   lah teek

mokopuna
moh koh poo nah

mwaar mwahr

fuchsia
   bright reddish
   purple

75

"Because wherever you look, you see ocean. You hear ocean. Whoosh, splashing every side near you. Everywhere, ocean!" Latik laughed. "Every side. You look north—ocean. East, west, even south, the same. Ocean all around."

Latik set down the *mwaar* she was weaving. She reached high above her head and then, down she swooped with both hands. "Like this the waves crash down from every side. Our island is only a little above the ocean and only a little bit across. "Whoosh. Whoosh. Always you hear the waves. Whoosh. You see them too. At low tide we walk from island to island. The water is only up to our knees."

Latik picked up the *mwaar*, began adding more flowers, and then nodded. "At low tide, we make a date with a friend. We make a *mwaar* of smell-good flowers. Even at night time. Plenty of us girls. We make a deal to go together. We cannot bring a boy to our home until we get married. That's why we go and hide. Make an excuse so we go to see our friends at another village on the nearby island. We wear our lava-lava and the smell-good flowers. In the evening we sneak away."

Then Latik frowned. Her dark eyes became even darker. She whispered as if afraid someone, or something, might hear her. "But if you go to my island, and you go out alone, come back home before dark." Again she whispered. *Before dark.* Or you won't come back."

"Why?" Goose bumps crawl up my arm. Chills and chicken skin!

"The ghost will kill you." Her face darkened and tilted downward, her eyebrows furrowed. There was not one spark of playfulness left in her voice.

"What ghost?"

"You cannot see the shape. Magic. *Mokopuna.* You fall down dead. You never come back."

More shivers. I knew she was not kidding.

"Now we talk story. Now I tell you how the beginning people came to my island. They came from Samoa. Yes, it is true. Long ago, when magic was strong. the chief of Samoa, a chief full of strong magic, had lost his wife. He knew she was some-where in the ocean. She had left Samoa in her canoe very angry with him. He had been searching for her.

"There she was! In the sea. She was already very weak, almost die, almost die. This great chief from Samoa, he used his magic to make islands so she doesn't die. He made all the Kapingamarangi islands so she can rest and not die. But when he was finished, again he could not find his wife. He knew she was somewhere on one of the islands. But where?

"The Samoan chief sailed back to Samoa and then returned with many of his people to these islands. He looked around. He felt strong magic. He was worried. He asked, 'Does someone live here already? If I go on an island that belongs to another, they will use magic to kill me.'

"He waited until night. All the men in his war canoe went on the island with him. They made a big fire. Then the chief waited to see if anyone made another fire.

"All around was the blackness of night, the blackness of the ocean. From all sides the whoosh of the waves. Sounded like it was about to crash over him. But then he saw a light. On the other side of the island, he saw the light of a big fire. He knew the ghost used his magic to make a fire.

"'We will move to another island.' he said. The next day they went to another island. In Kapingamarangi there are thirty-six islands. Every night the chief made a fire. Every night the ghost made a fire on the opposite end of the island. Every morning the chief and his men moved.

"He moved—moved—moved!

"Finally he heard a loud voice asking, 'Who are you? Who are you?'

"He said, 'I am the Samoan chief. I am looking for my wife and I am looking for my island.'

"The ghost replied, 'This island is mine. My grave is here.'

"The Samoan chief replied, 'I belong to here. This island belongs to me.'

"The ghost shouted back. 'Okay, we fight. We fight with magic.'

"'Yes, we fight. I am ready.' said the Samoan chief.

"The ghost shouted out. 'If you belong to here,

take this small island and move it over here.'

"The chief did.

"'Okay,' said the ghost. 'Take this other island and move it near the other island.'

"The chief did.

"Silence. No one spoke.

"The ghost shouted. 'So, we are the same. You take that island. That island I name **Touhou**, new island. That one is yours. Take it.'

"Silence.

"The ghost spoke again. 'This other island, **Vai'duah**. This one is mine. Remember this. What's happening there. That's yours. What's happening here, that's mine. Remember this.'

"The chief was unhappy. His island, Touhou, was very small. He needed a bigger island for his wife. He told his warriors. 'Measure the island. Go all around. Measure it.' They did.

"Now the chief said to the island. 'Grow bigger.'

"Every night, every night, the island grew bigger. Every day the chief told his men. 'Measure! Measure again.' Finally the island was big enough."

Touhou
  toh oo hoh

Vai'duah
  vye DOO ah

Latik looks at me. "That is the story of my island. You can go there and see the chief's grave. He was a very good chief. He lived there a long time with his wife. The church people built a church by his grave." She looks at me. "You will be scared. Whoosh. The waves look like they crash over you. From everywhere the waves are crashing."

I laughed. I kept thinking of standing on a tiny sandy atoll surrounded by crashing surf. Maybe I would tell someone, "Measure it. This atoll is too small. Make it bigger."

Latik picked up yellow blossoms to weave into the head wreath. "You will like my island. Plenty ocean. Plenty magic. Remember, if you go for a walk, come back before dark. Or you will fall down dead."

THE ORIGIN OF THE RAT CLAN

A long, long time ago, there were no rats on the island of Kosrae. Rat lived up in heaven. She lived with God. Her job was to tend a huge field of sugarcane. Rat was God's helper in his house and garden. She was fast and smart and always did as God asked. For these reasons, God liked her a lot and they got along well.

God decided to go away on a short trip. Only one day. He didn't think that would be a problem. So he asked Rat to watch over the sugarcane. "Oh yes," she said. "I will take the best care of your field that anyone could ever take." Rat went to the great field and lay down among the plants to rest. Then she heard a strange noise, just louder than a whisper: "Shuush, shuush, shuush." She stood up and looked around. But she couldn't see where the sound was coming from. So she lay down and waited. Again the noise came. Or was it just the breeze breathing heavily in the cane?

This time she stood up as fast as she could. She would catch that noise-maker! But as far as she could see there was nothing unusual, just a sea of green cane. She began to walk down the rows of plants. She got down on her knees and searched the ground. Then she stuck her nose between the rows of plants. She sniffed the warm air. But all she

Kosrae
kawz RYE ay

81

found were huge, ripe stalks of cane.

The noise became louder and louder! "Scritch, scritch, scritch." Rat put her ear up against a stalk of sugarcane. Slowly she walked around it. When she reached the place where it was loudest, she stopped. Gently, she leaned her ear against the cane. The noise was still louder!

What did Rat do? What would you have done? Well, Rat needed to find out what was so loud. It must be inside that stalk. So she bit the cane stalk right where the noise was coming from. What a surprise. Oh, sweetness! What a delicious taste in her mouth! This new taste was so sweet she kept on chewing, chewing, chewing, while she looked for what was making the noise. At last she discovered a tiny worm, so tiny she could barely see it.

Rat was very upset. What if the worm destroyed the entire field? She would have to check every stalk of cane for worms. If she found one, she would kill it. Besides, the cane was so sweet in her mouth. So she began to chew. Stalk after stalk, she chewed through the sugarcane field. She had many sharp teeth and was able to work very fast. Every single stalk of cane fell down flat. Now the sugarcane field looked like a sea of broken green sticks.

After all that chewing and eating, she had found only one worm. That was the tiny worm she saw on the very first plant. She saved that worm to show to God. It was proof of how the worm had nearly destroyed the field. Had it not been for her, the worm would have ruined everything! God would be happy with her.

When God returned, the field of tall, healthy cane was as flat as if a typhoon had roared through. Not a single stalk of sugarcane was standing! God rushed to find Rat. Rat began to explain, "A terrible thing almost happened. There was a noise in the cane. A worm was chewing up everything. If I hadn't searched and found that worm, the whole field could have been destroyed!"

Of course, Rat had ruined the entire field all by herself. God was so upset he yanked out her many teeth. He rammed two sticks of wood into her lower jaw. This was her punishment. Now she would be unable to destroy anything else. And this is how she is today, with only two long teeth in her mouth.

God was so angry he didn't want her near him any more. He put her in a basket and lowered her all the way to earth. The basket twisted and spun at the end of the very long rope. Rat cried as she left heaven, but God didn't change his mind.

Rat landed on the green, mountainous island of Kosrae. What a relief to climb out of the small basket at last. Slowly she made her way to the village of **Lelu**. But she wanted to be alone, away from people. She needed to think things over. She went to **Mutun Nenea** and climbed onto a big rock now called Rat's Rock. Many changes of the moon passed and then her life began to change. She got pregnant and had a beautiful baby girl. It was a human girl, with long hair and pretty brown skin. She looked just like the other Kosraeans. The girl grew up in secret—no one knew she was there.

One day, Rat's daughter went down to the ocean to bathe. She always did this in secret, as her mother had demanded. Rat's daughter had very, very long hair. It was longer than two women are tall. When she swam, the currents pulled it out to sea like a giant fishing net.

But this day the king of Kosrae was paddling by on his way from **Tafunsak** village to his home in Lelu. The beautiful girl didn't know the king was

Lelu   leh loo
Mutun Nenea
moo toon neh neh ah

Tafunsak
tah foon sahk

83

watching her. The sun sparkled in her wet hair. "Steer toward shore," the king ordered his people. "Take her on board." The instant the beautiful girl sat dripping in his canoe, her long hair trailing overboard, the king decided he was going to marry her.

This was the beginning of the Rat clan on Kosrae. It is said that this girl was the most beautiful of all the king's wives. It is also said that long ago, the Rat clan had the prettiest people on Kosrae. Today people are not so sure who is a descendant of that clan. Perhaps, just perhaps, you are one.

TEBWERE, TEBARERE, AND TETINTIRI

Once, on an island in Kiribati, three boys lived with their mother. The children were well taken care of, but they were not very obedient. They always ran away from their mother and did naughty things.

They lived on the north end of their island and were allowed to play in the **lagoon** all day. There was only one rule: They were NEVER to go to the south end of the island, for a giant lived there and would kill and eat them.

Of course, the boys could not wait to go to the south end of the island. One day, when their mother was taking a nap, they quietly ran out of their hut and down the path leading south. They did not believe the giant was real. Besides, they knew magic and could take care of themselves. Foolish children.

When they got to the south end of the island, they found a large pool of clear water that was full of fish. Just across the pool stood a hut. There was no one around. The boys were hot from their walk. The pool looked so good that before you could say, "Don't do that," they did. They jumped right into the pool and began to splash and play. By the time they were done, the clear water was all muddy.

Suddenly a large voice called out, "Who is playing in the giant's pool?" Then a huge old woman

Kiribati
KIH rih bus

Tebwere
teb weh reh

Tebarere
teb ah reh reh

Tetintiri
teh teen tee ree

lagoon
shallow body of water, often surrounded by a reef or an atoll

85

came out of the hut. "I see you naughty children! You are lucky that my husband is taking a nap! Now you better go away before you get into trouble."

The boys were not only naughty, but they were also rude. They teased the old woman and called her bad names. Now the woman was angry. "I will tell the giant about you and you will be in big trouble. Now tell me your names!"

"We are Tebwere, Tebarere, and Tetintiri," they answered. Then the silly children giggled and the youngest chanted a magic spell:

Old lady, old lady, this spell will tie
your tongue
And you will never tell by whom this
deed was done.

When the giant woke from his nap, he asked "Who dirtied my pool?"

"Three naughty boys," his wife replied.

"Well, tell me their names," demanded the giant. But his wife could only **stammer**. No matter how hard she tried she could not say the names of the boys.

The next day, the boys returned to the pool. This time they went fishing. They caught every one of the giant's special fish.

Once again the great voice boomed, "Who is there fishing in the giant's pool?" Once again the children cast their spell on the poor woman's tongue.

That night the giant went to his pool to catch some fish. The pool was empty. All the fish were gone. "Who has been catching my fish?" he demanded. His wife could only stammer. She could not tell him the names of the boys.

stammer
make unintended stops and repetitions in speaking

The next day was the worst day. The boys came once again to the giant's house. This time they cut down all of his coconut trees. The old woman was so angry! When the giant came home he saw what had happened. His wife could still not tell him the names of the boys.

The giant and his wife decided it was time to punish these boys. They began to follow the tracks the careless children had left in the sand. The tracks led straight to their little hut in the north!

Soon the giant and his wife came near the hut where the children lived. "I will catch you now!" the giant roared. He began to walk up to the hut. This time the youngest child's magic spell made the giant's feet walk away from the house. Although the giant started right toward the hut, he suddenly found himself on a beach far to the east. He had missed the hut entirely! "How did I get here?" he wondered. "I know the hut is in the north. I will be more careful." This time the giant found himself far to the west. No matter how hard he tried, his feet seemed to have a mind of their own and led him every place except to the hut.

This giant was not so stupid as the children thought. "Hmmmm," he thought. "My feet will not walk in a straight line. So maybe I will just crawl on my hands and knees. This way I will go right underneath their magic."

That is just what he did, right up to the hut. Then he ate the hut and everyone in it. And this is the end of my story, and the end of the foolish children as well.

MELANESIA

In the time before islands dotted the sea, a woman was captured by a snake. He held her prisoner so long she eventually gave birth to his son. She hated the snake. One day she poisoned him.

She didn't know he was a magical snake. At the place she buried him, water gushed out of the hill and became a clear, sweet stream. From his eyes grew a tree new to the world—a coconut tree.

The woman took special care of her son, even though he was the child of a snake. How carefully she bathed him, how tenderly she rubbed him with oil. She fed him nuts and fish to make him grow strong and fat. He knew who his father was, but he promised his mother never to tell anyone.

One day she found out her son had told his friends the secret of his birth. She was so angry she smashed the wall that held back the sea. A huge wave of water roared forth. It rushed over the land and tore trees up by their roots. The expanding sea swept everyone far, far away. It covered all the land except for a few tiny points, like a fistful of rocks strewn about. Many people died. Others washed up on island beaches where the ocean dropped them. Coconuts bobbed across the sea from the snake's grave toward distant islands.

This is one story about how the islands of Melanesia came to be. These islands are in the South Pacific, east of Indonesia and the continent of Asia. The islands span several thousand miles in the western Pacific, in a line that falls gently south as they move east, like the curl of a giant wave. "Melanesia" comes from the Greek words for "black" and "islands." Its earliest inhabitants had very dark skin and curly hair. Various groups of people now live in Melanesia, including Melanesians, Polynesians, Micronesians, and Europeans.

Melanesian civilization is older and more diverse than that of Polynesia or Micronesia. The original Melanesians migrated from Asia. The migration moved east, across the sea toward the rising sun. Today, Melanesians speak over a thousand languages. Most of these languages are native. A few are borrowed from peoples who occupied the islands.

Magical beliefs are common in the islands. **Busama** Island people believe their land is inside an upside-down bowl. To reach anyone else's land, people must climb this great bowl of heaven. The bowl is as strong and solid as roof-thatch, but what if it gets old and breaks? What will they do? Nobody knows, because it hasn't fallen yet. Sometimes the Melanesians of Papua New Guinea worry that sky

Busama
mboo SAHM ah

spirits will be washed down to earth by the rain. Who knows what tricks they will play if they wander the earth!

On some islands people believe that if you gaze into a deep, still pool, a spirit may steal your life by grabbing your reflection. People believe that your spirit leaves your body when you dream. It goes on a strange and marvelous journey. Your spirit knows it belongs to you, and always comes back before you wake. But if you die young, your spirit goes to a garden full of flowers.

In Melanesian stories, the sky spirits are as old as the sun. The earth is almost as old. In one story, a crocodile named Nuga slashes the land with his huge tail. Forever after, rivers flow from the cuts he made. Why did he attack the land? Legends tells us that his wife had been **lured** away. Great Nuga was so sad and angry he let loose his mighty tail. The great crocodile's sorrow changed the landscape forever.

lured
attracted by offering something

Another story, from the land of **Buka**, is about a couple paddling their canoe. When the woman steers, the shoreline slopes in soft curves. When the man steers, the shoreline is straight and hard. This story explains the way the land was formed. It also illustrates differences between women and men.

Buka   mboo kah

But how did people come to live on the earth? Some stories say we descended from the sky, looking much as we do today. Some say we were formed from sand or river mud, or that we grew out of the **segments** of a snake's tail. Some stories tell how we descended from animal ancestors, such as the iguana, snake, and pig. Still others say that in the beginning our creator carved a human figure out of wood. When he painted its face, its eyes fluttered open, and it became alive. Or, in one creepy story, clans

segments
separate pieces

wallaby
  small kangaroo

sacred
  worthy of
  respect

mana   mah nah

betel nut
  the seed of the
  betel palm,
  which, when
  chewed, acts
  like a drug

kava
  drink that acts
  like a drug

ridgepole
  highest horizon-
  tal timber of a
  roof

grew from maggots eating the corpse of a **wallaby** killed by the first human. Most of the stories tell the listener that creation often comes from an act of destruction, or from the actions of spirits.

As in other parts of the Pacific, the concept of taboo is very strong. A thing that is taboo is something so **sacred** it should never be harmed or even touched. If your clan is named after a giant clam or a crab or a bird, you must not eat that creature because it was once a living person. For Melanesians, another strong concept is *buto. Buto* is something so disgusting and awful it should never be touched

Mana is the word for power in much of the Pacific. It is especially important in Melanesia. *Mana* can live in people or in water, bones, animals, and rocks.

Mounds of stones lie on the graves of some of the most important ancient chiefs. The higher the pile of stones, the more important the chief. The power of Melanesian chiefs comes from their relationship to the spirit world. Ghosts and spirits are extremely powerful. They govern life and death. They can create violent storms or calm seas. Ghosts may take the form of sharks or almost any other animal.

Melanesians show respect for the dead by making offerings of food or other gifts, such as yam, **betel nut**, or **kava**. In earlier times, the way to show respect for a living person was to avoid using the person's name.

For Melanesians, spirituality and art are closely related. The islands have many rich artistic traditions. One is hammered bark cloth, or *tapa*, which many people wore as clothing. Other art includes carved masks, spears, and **ridgepoles**, and jewelry and body painting. The people create money from shells, woven mats, and feathers. Melanesians make music with drums, stringed instruments, **castanets**, and bamboo flutes. They tie small sacks of nuts and seeds on their wrists and ankles when they gather together to dance.

Long ago in parts of Melanesia, those who won a battle sometimes cooked and ate their enemies. They sometimes put the heads of their enemies on poles. Fijians explained this to outsiders as "the way of the land." They called their victims "long pig." Fijians gave up this practice long ago. Ever since, parents have told stories to their children about how and why this happened.

Melanesians have lived for thousands of years as fishing and farming people. The pig is a traditional unit of value. For example, a beautiful mat with many folds might be worth one pig with strong tusks. More important even than money is the *tabua*, or tooth of a sperm whale. A young man may offer *tabua* when he asks the family of a young woman if he can marry her.

tabua
tahm BOO ah

Many early Melanesian communities lived in isolation. Tall, rugged mountains, thick jungle, and roaring streams kept people from discovering their neighbors. That explains why Melanesian stories often focus on clans and community. The stories tell about home and families, how people came to be, and how they can live together peacefully.

Melanesia includes many island groups. Their total land mass is thousands of square miles. If you look at a map, you will see that some of the biggest Pacific islands are in Melanesia. There are also tiny coral atolls with delicate fringing reefs and coconut palms. Some islands have active volcanoes. Many contain huge mountains covered with **conifer** trees. The main island groups are known as Papua New

conifer evergreen

Guinea, Solomon Islands, Vanuatu, New Caledonia, and Fiji. Each island group has a unique history, so we must visit them separately.

PAPUA NEW GUINEA

Papua New Guinea is an independent nation. It shares part of its large main island with Indonesia. The southern tip of the island nearly touches the northern tip of Australia. In fact, Papua New Guinea and Australia were connected eight thousand years ago.

Papua New Guinea has volcanoes, grasslands, and reed-filled swamps. A wonderful variety of animals, from tree kangaroos to crocodiles, lives there. In the mountains, frost sometimes kills the sweet potatoes on which islanders depend for food. Like every Pacific island, Papua New Guinea has environmental concerns. Steep mountains, heavy rainfall, and growing population combine to cause soil erosion. The people are continuing to learn how to preserve Papua New Guinea's natural resources for the future.

Papuans have traditionally believed that the sky world is the same as the land world. A group of Papuan pygmies—small people—say that one of the sky spirits slid down a rope to earth in order to go fishing. When he wanted to go home, he discovered that someone had cut the rope! He cried so loudly his wife in heaven heard him. She felt sorry for him and threw down fire and delicious foods. The four cucumbers she threw down turned into women! They became his wives, the ancestors of important Papuan clans.

In certain rural areas, men and women live in separate houses. They live separately out of custom and respect for the differences between them. House styles vary depending on the climate. In warm, coastal places, houses are built on stilts over the water. In higher, colder regions, houses are dug deep into the ground.

The first settlers arrived perhaps forty thousand years ago. That was long before settlers arrived in other parts of Melanesia. Papua New Guinea has had a variety of rulers, including Britain, the Netherlands, Germany, and Australia. In 1975, the lush, dramatic islands finally celebrated their independence. Papua New Guinea remains an independent member of the British Commonwealth.

The people in Papua New Guinea speak over five hundred non-Austronesian languages. Austronesian languages are the languages most often spoken in the Pacific. Papua New Guineans have languages that developed earlier and differently from those of other Melanesians. Most Papuans speak the language of their ethnic group. Many also speak Tok Pisin, a "pidgin" language based on a mixture of English and native words.

People still live traditional lives. Most people live in the countryside as farmers. Of over seven hundred ethnic groups, more than eighty percent are Papuan. Most of the rest are Melanesian. Their economy once depended on tropical products such as cacao and coffee. Now they export minerals, natural gas, and oil. Perhaps as many as half of all adults cannot read. Sons are more likely to receive educations than daughters. Malaria, which is spread by certain kinds of mosquitoes, is a serious problem.

Legends tell us that Papua New Guinea is a place so rich and wonderful that long, long ago, the sky spirits came down to feast on its delicious foods. They thought they could stuff their bellies and go back to the sky. But they were wrong. Down below they learned about the great circle of life. They learned how all earth creatures are born and how, **ultimately**, all of us die so that others can be born.

ultimately
finally,
eventually

SOLOMON ISLANDS

Solomon Islands are a chain of coral atolls and volcanic islands. They are hot and humid, but trade winds often cool the islands. Most of the people are Melanesian. Though English is the official language, the people also speak more than sixty other languages. The islanders fish and farm for a living. Some also export palm oil and copra and the minerals bauxite (for making aluminum) and phosphate (for making fertilizer).

The first outsiders came from Spain in 1568. Spanish explorer **Álvaro de Mendaña de Neira** thought the biblical King Solomon had taken gold from these islands to build his temple in Jerusalem. He was wrong, but the name "Solomons" has remained ever since.

Álvaro de Mendaña de Neira
AHL vah roh day men DAHN yah day nay EE rah

Three hundred years later, Blackbeard the Pirate captured islanders. They were forced to work as slaves on farm plantations in Fiji and Australia.

In 1886, Germany and Britain divided up the islands between themselves. In 1942, during World War II, the Japanese took over the Solomons. A great battle was fought on Guadalcanal. The Americans won. After the war, the Solomon Islanders wanted independence. They finally achieved this in 1978. Today, the Solomons are a member of the British Commonwealth.

Like their sister islands, the Solomons have rich artistic traditions, such as carved wooden poles, bamboo drums and flutes, and unique dances. The people are deeply connected to the spirits. They believe people have two souls. One soul lives in the body. The other soul changes form, passing into sea and land animals, stones, trees, or fruit. As people grow old, their **totem** animal comes to them. This is their future form. If a person's soul belongs in the sea, his head—once he has died—may float in a carved wooden shark. When the right sea animal swims by, the soul joins it. Solomon Islanders believe their souls know how to find their new homes.

totem
representative of the clan, or family

VANUATU

Like most of Melanesia, Vanuatu has tall mountains, volcanoes, lowlands, and coral reefs. It has a hot, wet season and a cool, dry season. Vanuatu may be the most ethnically Melanesian of all of the island groups. The people speak over a hundred local Austronesian languages. The local religion is Christian, but also includes spiritism, or the worship of ancestors.

Vanuatu's people live mainly by fishing and farming. Although they now have a president, they also have a council of chiefs. Their constitution, written in 1980, says that the islanders cannot lose their traditional land. The people have a strong attachment to the land. As they do in ancient stories, men of a clan still gather to drink kava. They speak to the spirits of their ancestors, who are buried nearby.

These islands were settled relatively late, perhaps in 1400 B.C. Powerful kings later ruled the islands. They sometimes demanded human sacrifices for important political rituals. They may have buried some people alive.

Vanuatu was once controlled by the British and French together. It was known then as the New Hebrides. For long years until 1860s, outsiders forced many Vanuatu women and men to work on plantations in Fiji, New Caledonia, and Australia. This caused the people of Vanuatu, which means "Our Land Forever," to want independence. In 1980 they created the Republic of Vanuatu. In the hearts of these people, the land was never lost.

The stories from these islands teach important social rules. If you steal something valuable from others, they will take revenge on you, perhaps even kill you. You must respect the lives of others. You should even respect the knowledge of your enemies. Can you imagine what important skills rats teach people? Think of all the things rats can do with their sharp teeth. Then read "How the Rat Got Its Tail."

NEW CALEDONIA

cascading
falling steeply

New Caledonia has dramatic mountain ranges and **cascading** streams swollen by rain. It has dry grasslands and wet, salty mangrove swamps. The main island is known for its red soil full of minerals, such as nickel, cobalt, and chromium. As on many Pacific islands, once there were no mammals except for bats. Many rare species of birds live there. One is the *kagu*, which cannot fly.

kagu   kahn goo

People first settled New Caledonia about three thousand years ago. Europeans landed in the islands only two hundred years ago. In 1853, the French took control and are still in power today. They forced the islanders to work for them. They imposed taxes and **curfews.** Convicted criminals and political prisoners were brought in ships and forced to work for European landowners. Some of their descendants still live in the islands. Because New Caledonia depends on France for money, some people want to keep close ties with France. But many native people are working for independence.

curfews
times at which people are to be off the streets

Some stories from New Caledonia about animals

make them appear similar to people. In the story "The Seagull and the Mussels," the seagull and the mussels play "hide and seek." The mussels outsmart the seagull, reminding us that often we are fooled by looks.

Fiji

The islands of Fiji are volcanic islands. They "sit" on an underwater platform of rock. Forests, grasslands, fields of sugarcane, and tropical fruit trees cover these large islands. Mangrove swamps line the coasts.

The earliest settlers came from other Melanesian islands about 3,500 years ago. They brought food plants, pigs, and a special kind of pottery known as Lapita ware.

These first inhabitants were ruled by chiefs. Sometimes they made war on one another. Their weapons included spears, slings, clubs, axes, and poisoned arrows. They carefully carved spears. *Mana*, or power, could be put right where the arrowhead joins the slender shaft.

Early Fijians believed they came from stones, animals, caves, or spirits. Although they originally arrived by sea in sailing canoes, their myths say they have lived on Fiji forever.

In the 1600s, European explorers first sighted the islands. Famous explorers Captain James Cook and William Bligh visited Fiji. Bligh was captain of the ship *Bounty*, whose crew rebelled and abandoned him at sea. You can read about the crew's exciting adventures in "The Tale of the *Bounty*" in the Polynesia section of this book.

Europeans brought terrible diseases, including smallpox. Smallpox killed so many people the Fijians said the heavens turned the color of blood.

copra
dried coconut meat

Today, as they did long ago, Fijians grow fruits and vegetables. Today they also produce sugar, **copra**, cocoa, bananas, taro, and pineapple. They trade these crops for the goods of other nations.

Mosquitoes flourish during the rainy season in parts of Fiji. Legends say that long ago on Vanua Levu, people buried themselves in the sand in order to sleep peacefully.

In 1874, Fiji officially became a British Crown Colony after many years of British colonial rule. In the 1980s, it became an independent nation. Before World War II, many Indian laborers were brought to Fiji to work in the sugar industry. People who immigrated from India now outnumber the native people of Fiji. They and other groups of immigrants give Fiji a diverse racial heritage.

Fijians value their traditional arts. These include *tapa* cloth and mat weaving, canoe building, and woodcarving. Some old traditions live on, such as fire walking on hot coals. In the story "The Firewalkers of Beqa," you can learn more about this tradition.

The peoples of Melanesia have many things in common: colonial influence, island culture, fishing and farming, Austronesian (Pacific Island) languages, and respect for spirits, ancestors, magic, and ghosts. At the same time, the landscape of the islands, their populations and individual histories are different. Melanesia, the mother islands of the Pacific, holds its oldest stories and some of its deepest secrets.

KAMBEL CREATES THE WORLD

The people of western Papua call him **Gainjan**. He is the all-powerful spirit who created the world. His secret name is Kambel. Kambel married the sun, **Eram**, and together they had a daughter named **Gufa**, the moon that floats across the night sky.

In the beginning, the sky world was like an enormous sleeping platform. This platform did not hang from the heavens. It was held up from below by a **massive rattan** cane. If the sky creatures **quarreled** fiercely, the cane could snap. If the cane snapped, the sky would collapse, **deluging** earth with rain so heavy it would flood the land and drag the drowning land animals to the bottom of the sea.

One day in the ancient time of creation, Kambel decided to visit the earth. At that time it was an empty place, with no animals and no people. To get there, Kambel slid down to earth on a *sak'r* palm, a black palm that grows in **dense** forest. As Kambel slid, he heard strange sounds coming from inside the bark of the palm. He listened as hard as he could, but did not recognize the sounds. The sounds seemed to change as he slid farther down the tree. He listened and listened until he was so curious he couldn't stand it any more. When he reached the bottom, he whipped out his sharp-bladed axe and **hacked** down the tree.

Kambel
KAHM bel

Gainjan
GAYN jahn

Eram   EH rahm

Gufa
NGOO fah

massive very big

rattan
  a type of palm tree with strong stems

quarreled
  argued

deluging
  pouring water over

sak'r   SAH kur

dense
  growing closely together

hacked
  chopped at over and over

101

rumor murmur

Gambadi
ngam BAHN dee

Semariji
seh mah REE jee

Tandavi
tahn DAH vee

Keraki
keh RAH kee

Kambel began to walk up and down beside the fallen tree. At the top of the tree, he heard only a confused and faint rumble, a **rumor** of sound. Something was trying to get out. Kambel chopped the tree in half where the sound was loudest. His heart thumped in his throat! He could hardly believe what he saw. Out climbed the people who speak the **Gambadi** language of Papua.

Kambel slid his hands carefully down the tree, listening. Soon the sound changed, growing softer and higher like humming bees. Again he hacked open the black palm. Out came a whole tribe of people, the **Semariji**. Out they marched, singing the most beautiful song Kambel had ever heard.

Noise rose up again inside the palm. Voices rang in his ears, as if they were all howling, "Out, out, let us out!" He moved faster now, hacking and hacking. This time all the **Tandavi** people were uncovered. They stretched like butterflies in the sun, grateful to be free from the dark hollow of the tree.

Finally Kambel came to the bottom of the tree. One more huge cut and whack! Out came the **Keraki** people, clutching their newborn babies.

Kambel was pleased with his new family. "You are all my children," he proclaimed. "Welcome!" Then he told them which lands were to belong to each of them. The sky spirit sent all the tribes off in the direction of their new homes. Oh, he was tired from all that chopping! Weary, he climbed up a different tree to his resting place in the sky.

The world was not finished. There was yet much work to be done and many problems to fix. The sky and the earth were too close together. They were nearly pressing on each other. And besides, the sky was boring and empty. Kambel made a huge bonfire. He used the fire found in a hole under a special palm tree. When it was burning strongly, he roasted the woody center, or **nikup**, of the **sago palm**. When the *nikup* was hot and soft, he mashed it flat with his hands. With all his might, he heaved it up into the sky. The soft, cooked palm spread across the heavens, forming the soft sago clouds.

Next he **kneaded** small balls of the *nikup*. He roasted them in the fire until they turned into rock. He gave these to the people of the **Bangu** tribe. The Bangu use these round stones in ceremonies to call down the rain.

Even with clouds and rain, the sky was still too close to the earth. Now Kambel threw his weight against the rattan cane and pushed as hard and as high as he could. The sky rose up, up, up and a fresh cool breeze blew around his head. Kambel admired all the new space. Still, something wasn't right. His heart felt lonely when he looked up. So Kambel the creator threw many small pieces of bamboo, or **kajen**, into the air. The pieces turned into bright, twinkling stars. Watch them tonight, sprinkled like magic dust across the night sky.

When all this was done, and the moon and sun and stars were in place, Kambel remembered the earth. Not much grew there. At that time, coconuts grew in the earth like yams and taro. Kambel wanted to be able to watch their thick green husks ripen, so he would know when they were ready to harvest. He found a tall pole and hung coconuts on it. Ever since, coconuts have grown from the ground on tall, thin trees.

When Kambel finished **sculpting** the earth and causing freshwater rivers to run down its green valleys, he admired his work. But it was not enough: people and other creatures had to have food to eat. Kambel set to work forming the roots of the taro,

nikup NEE koop

sago palm
(SAY go) a palm that produces a powered starch used in foods and to stiffen cloth

kneaded
pressed with the hands

Bangu
MBANG goo

kajen
KAH jehn

sculpting
carving, molding

petrels
  small long-
  winged seabirds

curlews
  brown birds
  with long legs
  and down-
  curved bills

pollinate
  place pollen on,
  in order to
  fertilize

slunk
  moved in a
  secretive way,
  as if fearful or
  shameful

Tumbabw'r
toom BAHB wur

slithered
  slipped or slid
  in a back-and-
  forth motion

shriveled
  dried up and
  became
  wrinkled

yam, and banana plants with his bare hands. He created insects for **petrels** and **curlews** to eat, bees to **pollinate** the hibiscus blossoms, and fish for the humans to roast upon their cookfires.

Kambel was very weary from all this creation. He lay down to sleep and let the earth creatures explore their new world.

Days later, he awoke and looked around, remembering all that he had done. The green valley looked the same as he remembered, but then a strange creature crawled out from under a rock. It had two heads and long fangs reaching below its chin. He hadn't made this creature! Where had it come from? How had it been born?

Kambel didn't kill the beast. Instead he sat and watched as the young earth came alive with new life, the good creatures he had created and the other ones who appeared out of nowhere. Mysterious four-footed beasts **slunk** out of caves and wandered off into the world. Kambel realized that life was more than his creation. It grew from other life, changing form. Most was good, but some of it was evil.

Then something really frightening happened. In the hole under the palm where fire crackled for the first time, an enormous creature stirred. The great **Tumbabw'r slithered** out, a long, snaky monster. Its enormous head rose from inside the hole and flopped onto the ground. Salt water flowed from its mouth! Kambel didn't know what to do. This was the most frightening creature he had ever seen. He watched the Tumbabw'r for a long time. Its long, forked tongue spat poison. Before Kambel's eyes, a beautiful bush covered with yellow blossoms **shriveled** and died when a single drop of poisonous saliva dripped on it.

This poison would kill Kambel's creatures. The Tumbabw'r had to be stopped. Kambel reached into his **quiver**. Arrow after arrow flew toward the Tumbabw'r's head! But the arrows didn't even pierce the flesh of this giant, **writhing** eel. It opened its mouth and groaned. The smell of rotten meat filled the air. The monster began to move toward Kambel! He lunged for his strongest spear and plunged it into the eel's dark, scaly head.

Salt water gushed from the wound, tearing it open. Water swirled around Kambel. He ran to keep from being swallowed by its great, sucking mouth. Water spread and spread until it had filled the whole south part of the world. Kambel ran as fast as the wind, the water rushing at his heels. Finally he got ahead of the widening flood. At **Tarekor**, where the **Tivrav'r** plant grows, he was able to stop and rest for a moment. How his chest ached from running. His heart banged in his throat. All of his creatures, whom he had sworn to protect, would be drowned!

Water raced along the ground, rising higher and higher. It was almost up to Kambel's neck! He tore loose the heavy branches of the Tivrav'r tree and used them to push back the floodwaters. With all his strength, he pushed and pushed. The branches snapped and Kambel tore loose new ones. He worked harder than he ever had before, harder than when he had created all living things. His breath came in great, exhausted gasps. But at last the water was pushed back to the sea. The Tumbabw'r drowned in his own flood. Kambel found the rotting body days later and ordered the tribal chiefs to come together and bury the giant eel.

Today, there is still a small trickle, a river that rose up at that place—the **Wassi Kussa** River. If brave Kambel hadn't stopped the floodwaters, the

quiver
case for holding arrows

writhing
twisting, as if in pain

Tarekor
tah reh kor
Tivrav'r
teev RAH vur

Wassi Kussa
WAH see KOOS sah

roiling
  stirring up mud

earth would be covered completely with **roiling** blue water and foaming whitecaps. Instead, the earth is covered with living things. Many of them are still singing the song the Semariji sang when they walked out of the black log. It is the song they sang in the sunlight to celebrate the day they were born into the world.

THE CIRCLE OF BIRTH AND DEATH

In Papua New Guinea, the tops of the mountains pierce a layer of clouds. As if they had eyes, the mountaintops quietly observe the sky spirits. Down below, the mountains' rocky roots feel the yams growing. Their dusty sides echo with the sound of people stamp-stamping their dances.

The people of the high mountains of **Simbang** say there was a time when all humans lived in the sky. This was because the earth was new and its surface was still very hot. The sleeping-platforms of all people were way up above the clouds. People lived forever. Time did not exist. Every day was the same as every other. Some of the people, especially the young, quick-footed ones, began to grow restless. "Please papa," begged a sky child. "Can't we just do something?"

A huge lizard lived in the sky. It was said that he was wise. But it was also said that every so often he told big, fat lies. Most of the time he was helpful. Once in a while he did something cruel. Because everyone lived forever, they needed to forgive when bad things happened.

When the earth had cooled and living things rooted and grew in its soil, the lizard told the sky people tales of amazing food and brilliant beauty. All this existed on earth! Earth's land **cradled** all the

Simbang
SIM bang

cradled
held protectively

107

warblers
  songbirds

colors of the rainbow. Sweet songs flowed from brooks, **warblers**, and wind shush-shushing through pine trees. Earth offered sweet coconuts to drink and plenty of tender coconut meat to eat. Even fire! How delicious it was to roast yams.

sassy
  bold, cocky

Pigs and dogs ran through the forests. Fat, **sassy** birds laid eggs. Flowers to tuck behind your ears blanketed the meadows. Slippery fish with glassy eyes swam in the streams. Earth's lakes were like mirrors. Even the caves echoed your name when you called out to them.

shinny
  move up or
  down a pole

The lizard told how to visit earth: slide down a long, thin bamboo pole. **Shinny**, shinny, slide! Down to earth you slipped and slid. The people were so excited they could barely wait their turn to slide down the bamboo pole.

"But how do we get back home?" a man asked.

"Yes," said another. "We can't go unless we can come back home again."

"Oh, that's easy," said the giant lizard, his mouth crooked open in a smile. "Just climb back up the pole. I'll make it easy for you—I'll put notches in it like the steps of a ladder. See?" He **slithered** over and **gnawed** a perfect step into the pole.

slithered
  slipped or slid
  in a back-and-
  forth motion

gnawed
  chewed away
  bit by bit

"Thank you," said the sky people. Not everyone went. Some believed the lizard's words and some didn't. But many, oh so many, chose to go! One by one they wrapped their hands around the sturdy pole, jumped free of the clouds, and down they slid. They were so busy holding on tight they didn't see the lizard laughing at them.

bobbled moved
up and down over
and over

luscious delicious

Earth was gorgeous. Fresh, cool water bubbled up out of the ground. Orange-red bird-of-paradise blossoms **bobbled** in the breeze. Everything the lizard had said was true! The people harvested yams and **luscious** red fruits hanging from trees. They lit a huge fire and watched it dance and wave like the arms of a hundred happy girls.

Later, when they had explored and were ready to rest, the sky people baked their yams in the glowing coals. In the shade of a silvery-green acacia tree they feasted. The young people danced and sang while their parents warmed themselves before the fire. After the feast, they swam once more in the rivers. They took the burning sticks of fire into the caves and drew **sooty** pictures on the walls.

But then something terrible happened. One of the children stepped on an ant and crushed it. "Get up!" said the child to the ant.

The ant didn't move. It lay in flat black pieces at the child's feet. "Papa," cried the child, "Why won't it get up?" She thought all living things lived forever like the sky people. The little creature should wake up and march across the sand.

Gently the father lifted the dead ant. Other ants **scurried** about, frightened by his huge human shadow. He reached down and smashed another ant between his fingers. All movement stopped. The man watched and waited. Suddenly he screamed a spine-curdling yell. The tribe came running.

"What's the matter?" they yelled.

"This creature—" The boy's father was panting now. "It—it—it won't move. It is no more." There was no word in their language for death, so he could not even say that it had died. The people began to tremble. What kind of world had they come to?

Together they carved spears and hunted a bird, a gecko, and a pig. "We honor your spirit, living creature. May you live forever," they chanted. Then they took a heavy rock and killed the bird, the gecko, and the pig. The pig's dark blood **gushed** from its neck into the sand. Prayers drifted away in

sooty
made of the fine black powder produced by burning

scurried
rushed about in an excited manner

gushed
poured out suddenly

the evening wind. Nothing could bring these creatures back to life.

This is not what the lizard had told them! Liar! Nothing lasted here. The bees made their honey and then they died. The flowers bloomed and their open faces **shriveled**. Dogs and pigs and even wives grew old and died.

Too late for the people from heaven! They had eaten the food of the earth. Now they too would experience all of earth's gifts, even the bitter ones: birth, sickness, old age, and death.

The sky people **huddled** together and wept. One brave woman said, "Don't give up! We must climb back to the sky. We don't need these full bellies. It is better to live forever!" The people ran to where the bamboo pole had been stuck into the ground. It must still be there, waiting for them to slip their toes into the carved notches and climb hand over hand back to heaven.

But no! The evil lizard had bitten the bamboo pole clear through. It lay in pieces on the ground, splintered and still dripping with his saliva. "Look!" cried the man who had asked the lizard how they would return to the sky. "He didn't even carve the notches! All the time he was planning to leave us here!"

Sadly, the people turned away. The sound of weeping grew dimmer and dimmer as small groups wandered off by themselves. One followed the snaky curves of the river bank. Another group walked under the **canopy** of broad-leafed trees. A third one climbed up into the hills that led to the mountains.

They were the **ancestors** of the people who live on earth today. Because of them you were born. And because our home is the earth, living things will experience forever the great cycle of birth and death.

shriveled
dried up and became wrinkled

huddled
gathered closely together

canopy
protective covering

ancestors
family members who came before, like great-great-grandparents

THE JEALOUS SUN AND HIS BELOVED MOON

While walking in the forest one day, **Aruako** discovered a beautiful girl alone in a pond, taking her bath. Her grass skirt lay folded near the pond's edge. He sat down on it to watch her. Her lovely wet skin **shimmered** in the sunlight. Underneath the pond's clear surface, her body moved as gracefully as a **mermaid**'s. She looked like a woman, but she was actually the spirit of the moon.

The moon woman spied Aruako sitting on the bank. "I remember you," she said. "You dug me like a root from the side of my mother earth." Then she threw back her head and laughed! "You poor thing, burning with desire! You want to marry me. But I warn you—you will die! I am a spirit and you are a man. We can never marry."

Aruako listened but paid no attention to her words. They were as light as butterfly wings on his cheeks. He was **enchanted** by her radiant beauty. How she glowed with light!

The moon maiden watched Aruako watching her. "I know what you're thinking," she said. "This pond is filled with magic. I come here each day to wash myself and **restore** my brightness. You had better get those **reckless** thoughts out of your head, you foolish man. I am **betrothed** to the sun. Only he can marry me." She stared at him with her dark,

Aruako
ah roo AH koh

shimmered
shone like silk
or satin

mermaid
creature with
the body of a
woman and a
fish's tail

enchanted
charmed

restore
bring back

reckless
not carefully
thought out

betrothed
engaged to be
married

111

liquid eyes.

"Wait," pleaded Aruako. "Listen to me. I unearthed you. I found you and set you free. You are so beautiful. Surely you belong to me. I will marry you."

He took her by the hand and led her deep into the forest. At first she tugged against his hand. She knew she shouldn't go. But he was gentle and his eyes shone with joy when he looked at her. Step by step they walked on.

He had a house in the deepest part of the forest. He led the moon spirit inside. Slowly, slowly, he began to stroke her long, shiny hair. The moon maiden sighed deeply. She laid her head on his shoulder. Gently he stroked her back. Gently she returned his **caresses**. For this night, she was his. They slept side by side, breathing in rhythm. The stars **pulsed** brightly in the sky, while the moon slept with her human lover. The night was calm, as if even the breeze had gone to bed. Everywhere creatures slept in peace.

But then the sun began to rise in the east, already boiling with rage.

When Aruako opened his eyes, he shivered. Then he remembered. The moon maiden! He reached across the sleeping mat, but her warmth and smooth skin were gone. The lovely spirit of the moon had left him. He ran through the forest calling her name. He dove into the pond and searched among the rocks at the bottom. Nowhere could he find her.

The sun grew fiery, pouring his hot anger onto Aruako. Soon Aruako was dizzy with the heat. Staggering, he fainted. Then he woke up and began to crawl on his hands and knees toward his village. The earth seemed to well up as if it had turned into

caresses
loving touches

pulsed
shone in short, regular flashes

sea swells. The heavy hot air almost suffocated him.

Two boys found him collapsed upon the path to the village. He was barely breathing. They ran to tell the villagers.

Aruako's skin was pale and dry. His eyes rolled back in his head. "He's terribly sick," said a woman. "Bitten by an adder snake, he was. No one survives that. Or maybe he has sun sickness."

"Lift him," commanded the chief's son. "Carry him home."

"Do what you can for him," the chief told Aruako's family. They prepared cool **compresses** of water-soaked leaves. They brought him food and water, but he was too sick to eat or drink. He lay nearly lifeless in the shade. His eyes fluttered open. He tried to swallow sips of water. Girls fanned him with palm fronds. His mother and sisters sat near and sang healing chants softly near his ears.

compresses
folded cloths pressed against a body part to aid healing

But the sun rose ever higher and hotter in the sky. Light sneaked under the palm-leaf fans, burning Aruako's skin. His skin blistered and bubbled and then turned black and dry as charcoal in a dead fire. The tears in his eyes dried up. His tongue swelled and filled his mouth.

"Feel him," said his mother to her sisters, looking fearfully up at the sun. "He is boiling inside. The sun plans to kill him. See how it sneaks under our fans and destroys the shade!" All day poor Aruako lay there, sicker and sicker, weaker and weaker.

Finally, the sun was satisfied. It sank down to the western horizon and slipped over the edge of the world. The moon with her gentle glow uncovered her lovely face. But it was too late for Aruako. Just as the moon **peered** lovingly down at him, he died. Today, the people of his village turn their faces away from the moon. They remember the jealousy of the sun. They will not risk his **wrath** by gazing too long on the face of his beloved moon.

peered looked

wrath anger

114

THE WARRIOR WOMEN OF LUMALAO

Tales from Solomon Islands often seem "darker" than tales from many other islands. These stories involve **cannibalism**, killing, and black magic. Spirits live not only in the sea but also in the dark woods. Huge, dark, threatening forests cover many of the islands in the Solomons. These forests are often **sacred**, with the ghosts of **ancestors** living in **groves** of giant trees.

Once, in the time before, ghosts, called *gosile*, flew about the sky looking for humans to eat. They loved the taste of uncooked flesh. Especially brains. When they flew, the wind rushed through their long hair, making an **eerie** noise—"*Whooeeeeiii.*" Those who heard this sound knew that *gosile* were nearby.

On this one day, two young women were walking near their village. They strolled together, picking flowers and talking about their husbands and their families.

Suddenly, **disaster** struck. Two *gosile* were flying high overhead. They were feeling a bit hungry. When the first, **Otabulau**, looked down, he saw the two women on the road far below. "Look at that," he said to his companion, **Nuitarara**. "I think I see our dinner walking down that road!"

With that, the two *gosile* flew down and captured the women. Now *gosile* are very strong, and it did

Lumalao
loo mah LOW
cannibalism
the eating of human flesh by other humans

sacred
worthy of respect

ancestors
family members who came before, like great-great-grandparents

groves
small forests

gosile
goh SEE leh

eerie
frightening, strange

disaster
a sudden event causing great loss or damage

Otabulau
oh tam BOO low

Nuitarara
noo ee tah RAH rah

no good for the women to resist. They cried and screamed, but the *gosile* carried them off.

The *gosile* flew to their home on **Saraainonganonga**, far out in the ocean. There they set their **captives** down while they sharpened their stone axes. When the women realized that the axes were going to be used to cut them up into little pieces, they began to cry even louder.

"Please don't eat us!" they cried. And the two *gosile*, who weren't all that hungry, decided not to eat them. Instead, they even helped the women learn to fly so that other *gosile* could not catch and eat them. They did this by cutting the women's feet and draining out all the heavy blood. But they would not let the women return to their homes.

The *gosile* tried to give the women some uncooked flesh for dinner, but the women refused to eat it. They even refused the brains! The *gosile* were puzzled, since that was the very best part.

So the *gosile* found other food, like fish, and cooked it for the women. But the *gosile* did not eat that kind of food. Not at all!

Every day the *gosile* flew off to catch fresh fish for the women. They also flew off to capture fresh humans to eat. One day they brought back the bodies of two of the women's close relatives. The men were already dead, so there was nothing the women could do.

Another day, the women's husbands organized a rescue party. A huge reward was offered for the safe return of the women and the killing of the evil *gosile.* Young **betel nut** trees, coconuts, porpoise teeth, pigs with huge tusks, and, most valuable, one hundred strings of shell money, would be given to the warrior who killed the monsters.

Many tried, and failed, to claim this reward. A

Saraainonganonga
sah rah ah ee
NAHNG uh
NAHNG uh

captives prisoners

betel nut
the seed of the betel palm, which, when chewed, acts like a drug

116

rescue party of one hundred canoes returned empty-handed. Many of the crew had been carried off by the *gosile*. The villagers gave up hope.

"What can we do?" they asked. "The *gosile* are stronger than any man." The husbands, **Gwaufiu** and **Uluirara**, **lamented**: "Is no man strong enough to defeat these *gosile*?"

On Saraainonganonga, the two wives, **Raronaia** and **Araanaia**, cried out: "Is there no man to save us from these monsters?"

There wasn't.

But there was a woman.

Word of the plight of the women, and of the huge reward offered for their rescue, spread far and wide. One day it reached the island of Lumalao. There lived a fierce group of warrior women and their leader, **Riina**.

"Is this true?" wondered Riina. "Is this large reward offered just for killing two *gosile*?"

Riina traveled to the island of the husbands and offered to kill the *gosile*. The villagers thought she was **boasting**. This made Riina very angry. She stamped her feet and announced, "These are just *gosile*. And male *gosile* at that! I am stronger, and I will break their jaws!"

With that, Riina paddled back to Lumalao and gathered her large fighting group of women. Together they set out looking for the *gosile* island.

The band paddled from island to island. Finally they neared the island of Saraainonganonga.

"*Whooeeeeiii.*"

The eerie sound floated over the waves. "This is the place," announced Riina. "Everyone hide." Riina alone stood up in the canoe. When the *gosile* saw a canoe approaching with only a single woman, they were not concerned. One of the *gosile*,

Gwaufiu
ngwow FEE oo

Uluirara
oo loo ee RAH rah

lamented
said with sorrow

Raronaia
rah roh nah EE uh

Araanaia
ah rah ah nah EE uh

Riina
ree EE nah

boasting
bragging

Otabulau, flew down at her carrying his sharp stone axe. He intended to kill Riina and eat her for his supper!

Instead, Riina grabbed Otabulau's hair and threw him into the canoe. There all of the other women tied him up in the bottom of the boat.

"Where do you get your power?" she asked. The frightened *gosile* replied, "From betel, lime, and my red stone axe." As he spoke these words, these very objects fell from his body into the bottom of the canoe.

Riina carefully and slowly stepped right over these sacred objects.

taboo
forbidden, not allowed

essence nature

bound tied up

It was, of course, **taboo** for any woman to step over sacred objects. When Riina stepped over the objects, her female **essence** instantly took away all of the power of Otabulau's axe, betel, and lime.

The canoe landed. The women took the **bound** Otabulau and climbed to the *gosile*'s cave. Nuitarara, the second gosile, stayed nearby. In the cave, the women found a **ghastly** sight. Rows and rows of skulls, some still with fresh flesh, lined the walls.

ghastly
horrible, terrifying

Riina was outraged. She suddenly turned on the gosile and drew out her special weapon. A **boomerang**!

boomerang
a throwing club bent so that it returns to the thrower

startled surprised

With this weapon she struck the **startled** gosile and killed them both in an instant. Riina kicked down the rows of terrible skulls. Then she took the two captive women and began the long trip back to their island.

It took six days of paddling to get back to the village. The husbands and village were so happy to get their wives back and be rid of the *gosile* that they prepared a huge feast.

Thus these warrior women did what no man had been able to do. Many other tales are told of Riina and her band, but they must be kept for another time.

HOW THE RAT GOT ITS TAIL

In the islands of Vanuatu, a flock of seabirds decided to build a canoe. They had never built a canoe before so they held a long talking meeting. What should they do first? They chose a breadfruit tree. First they flew around its branches, fluttering their wings and all asking a question at once: "Strong, generous tree, we ask your spirit permission to help us in our **quest**. We seek to build a canoe and explore new lands. Will you come with us out over the blue ocean?" The tree spirit whispered its willingness to help them. Together, like a giant army, they **gnawed** through the thick trunk of the tree. It smashed against the forest floor with a huge thud. But then they discovered a terrible problem. Even working together, their wings flapping and flapping, they could not move the heavy tree. If they could not move it, how could they ever paddle it as a canoe?

The birds left the breadfruit tree and flew farther into the forest. With their sharp beaks, they chewed through a stalk of giant taro. Together they hollowed out the taro stalk. At last—a beautiful canoe! They had built their boat. Now they wanted to go to sea.

They needed a **navigator**, a captain to be their leader at sea. But who would be captain?

Just as they were pushing their canoe into the

quest
adventurous journey

gnawed chewed

navigator
person who steers a boat

water, along came a rat. This rat had a very high opinion of himself. "Stop everything and listen to me!" he commanded. "I shall be captain of the ship." The birds didn't think this was fair. They began to argue with the rat.

"You'll be sorry!" snapped the rat, and began to bite the **hull** of the canoe.

"Oh no, it'll be ruined!" a tern yelled.

"Let the stupid rat have his way!" said a red-footed booby. The rest agreed.

And so the birds let the rat be captain of their canoe. Together they flapped their wings and pushed their canoe out into the lagoon. Then they raised their leaf-paddles and began to make for the open sea. The rat was a bad captain. Pretty soon he and the birds were arguing again.

"I told you to paddle on the sunny side!" yelled the rat. "You stupid birds, you don't even have arms!"

"You said cloudy side," said a kingfisher. "We all heard you, right?" he said, looking at the other birds for approval.

hull
   frame and outer covering

120

"Mmmmm hmmmm," they all murmured.

"I'd be better off without a crew!" yelled the rat. Then he tried to bite a shy little starling.

"Ouch!" she screamed, burying her head under her wing. The mighty kingfisher became so angry he thrust his beak through the hull of the canoe. Seawater rushed in, **swamping** the boat. Slowly it began to sink.

With a great flapping of wings, the seabirds rose into the blue sky. They watched their canoe disappear under the water. The rat **thrashed** and gasped in the salty water. They didn't care. They thought the nasty rat deserved to drown. The rat tried to swim, but he barely knew how. He sank, bobbed up, and sank down again.

A sea turtle swam by just as the rat's head bobbed up. "Oh turtle, take me with you," pleaded the rat. The rat was choking on water. Again he disappeared, as if pulled down by sea **demons** from below. But the turtle turned his broad back and swam on.

Then an octopus swam by. "Friend octopus, I am drowning!" cried the rat, who had surfaced one last time.

The octopus hesitated and looked back over her soft shoulder at the rat. She didn't like his long, pointy nose or his beady black eyes. But he was a creature and he was drowning. She had a good heart. "Climb up on my back. I will keep you from drowning." The rat hung onto her soft, slimy back with his sharp little claws. How they hurt the octopus! Slowly she swam toward the distant shore. The beach was a thin white line gleaming between the blue of the ocean and the green of the land.

The rat was already feeling better and he began to laugh. He couldn't help it. He thought it funny

swamping
filling with water

thrashed
moved about violently

demons
evil spirits

the way the octopus's head rose up and down as they crossed each wave.

The octopus didn't like this. "What are you laughing about?" she asked.

"Nothing," he lied. "At least, I'm not laughing at you!" Then he laughed even harder.

The octopus didn't like the rat. She didn't like his claws digging into her soft flesh. Still, she took him all the way to the beach.

Once he was safely on land, the rat said, "Thanks for the ride, slime-face. Now I'm going to take a long bath and try to get your bad smell off my fur." The octopus's green body flushed purple with anger! With one of her long arms, she snatched up a stick. She whacked the rat as hard as she could. One end stuck in his back.

"Ouch!" he screamed.

"You ungrateful creature," the octopus hissed. "I could have left you out there. You'd be dead, floating at the bottom with the sea cucumbers. A shark with razor-sharp teeth would eat you for lunch."

"You slimy blob! Get that ugly face of yours underwater where it belongs," yelled the rat. Then he gobbled up some ashes from an old cooking fire. He spat them right onto the octopus's head. She howled with rage, but she couldn't go any farther onto the land. She threw sand into the nasty rat's eyes, slid into the water as fast as she could, and swam away.

And this is why the rat now has a long, spiky tail and the octopus has black stains on the top of her head. To this day, they don't speak. The rat stays on land. The octopus stays in the sea.

WHY PEOPLE HAVE TO DIE

Once there was a young boy who loved his grandmother very much. He was so small she often held his hand as they walked. Every day they walked under the leafy forest **canopy** to the bathing pool. There, the river was wide and slow. On the day that changed human lives forever, the birds were singing, "treee-kik, treee-kik." It was spring, and purple trumpet-flowers lifted their open faces to the sun. No one knew that death was coming.

canopy
protective covering

The grandmother spread her best woven mat on the ground. She sat the child on it. "Stay here while I bathe," she said. "The river is cool, clear, and deep. Don't go in the water. Just wait for me."

Then she did a shocking thing. She crawled out from inside her old skin. It was full of wrinkles and hung limply around her knees and elbows. Even her cheeks sagged, like overripe fruit. The grandmother dropped her old skin on the ground as if she were throwing away the empty husk of a coconut. "I'll be back soon," she said to her little grandson. Then she slipped into the cool, fresh water.

Sunlight sparkled on the lazy water. Her grandson watched her splash. Soon she was clean, and she came back to him. "You see," she said, "I wasn't gone long, was I?"

He didn't answer. He stared at her with terrified

eyes.

"Let's go. I'll take you home to your brothers now." The boy stared and stared. His lip began to tremble. He had never seen his grandmother without her skin. He didn't recognize this young woman. Her skin was young and tight, like his own. Her face was rosy and smooth. She was pretty, but he didn't want to go with her. Not this stranger. When she reached out her hand for his, he shrank down against the ground.

"What?" she said. "Are you afraid of me, my little one? I'm your grandmother. Do you think you don't know me? Remember how we picked berries in the woods? How you found fire ants inside that rotting log? How we sang the starling's song?"

The little boy was too scared to speak. He wanted only one thing: for his own grandmother to come back. He didn't like this strange woman at all.

His grandmother sat down next to him. Her head hung down in sorrow. How much she wanted to be young and beautiful again! But she knew now that it couldn't be. She sighed a long, deep sigh. Gently, she picked up her old, wrinkled skin and dusted it off. Slowly, she put it on again. Her face sagged. Her brow was lined with age and worry. Her young, quick feet became flat and stiff to walk on. Even her belly swelled out in front of her.

The old woman sighed. "For love of the children, so it must be."

THE THIEVES WHO HELPED INVENT THE CANOE

Nobody lived on the tiny island of **Vao**. But long ago, one very dark night, the people of **Mallikolo** heard strange noises coming from Vao. **Wailing** and screeching began just as the moon rose from her dark sleeping-bed. The people tried to shut their ears to the frightening sounds. Every night the sad sounds drifted across the **lagoon**. No one wanted to go to Vao, not even during the day. Besides, the only way to get there was to swim. No one wanted to do that.

One morning, the villagers discovered that the food they had cooked for breakfast was missing. It was stolen during the night. The next day more food was missing. Fresh rockfish, steamed taro wrapped in banana leaves, even raw yams hidden under heavy stones.

The chief ordered guards posted. All night the people took turns waiting and watching for the thief. They saw nothing, even when they kept the cookfires burning all night long. But every morning, more food was missing.

One morning a shrill cry sliced through the air. "Aaaaack!" shrieked a woman. People gathered around her hut. "Look! My toe!" Her big toe was gone. A raw red stump was all that was left. Her mat was stained with blood.

Vao   vow

Mallikolo
mal lee KOH loh
wailing crying out

lagoon
    shallow body of
    water, often sur-
    rounded by a
    reef

sorcerers
  magicians who
  call on evil
  spirits for help

The chief called a meeting of his wisest **sorcerers**. Who had done such a terrible thing? It must be one of their own if the guards never saw the thief coming or going at night. After much talk, the sorcerers pointed at a young man and said, "That one! He did it! He must be punished."

The villagers tied the frightened young man to a tree with thick palm rope. Then they began to prepare for a great feast. They would roast and eat the thief, as was their custom.

The young man's mother begged the chief to show mercy. "You have the wrong one," she cried. "Oh my chief, you have tied up an innocent boy."

"I see you love your son as mothers do, but the council knows of his guilt. Your son is the thief who must die," said the chief. That very night a child woke shrieking in his hut. Blood was pooling on his sleeping mat. Two small toes had been chewed completely off!

"I heard the sound, scritch, scritch, scritch," said the boy's sister, her wide eyes white with fear.

"Everyone back to bed," commanded the chief. "Wrap your feet in leaves. Post guards." But that same night, as the morning star shone overhead, the chief's wife cried out. In her dream, she had been nursing her child. But when she woke, something was actually walking on her breasts! Soon the whole village was awake again. They whispered among themselves. Many stories were passed from hut to hut. An evil spirit had come to live among them.

The next day, the mother of the young man doomed to death came again to the chief. "I beg you," she said. "Spare my son. He could not have committed these crimes. He was tied up and guarded all night long."

"This is true," said the chief. "He will be spared

for now. But if he is an evil spirit, he will be punished. You are right. We must be sure."

Many days and nights passed. The golden moon grew fat and then slender again. More yams, taro, and toes were gobbled up during the night. No one knew what to do.

One morning just at dawn a guard noticed a black shadow speeding along the ground. He chased after it—faster, faster, so it wouldn't escape! The shadow was a large rat. It leaped onto a piece of wood and floated quickly toward the island of Vao.

That very morning, the chief ordered several men to swim to Vao. "Swim, my men," he ordered. "Bring back the missing toes." The men did not want to swim. They were afraid of sharks and slimy creatures that live in sea caves.

How could they cross the lagoon to Vao without swimming? They had to obey the chief. So they did what the rats had done: they built a raft. The guard who had seen the large rat described its raft. The village men cut down eight strong bamboo stalks with their stone axes. Together they lashed together the hollow logs with woven coconut rope. Then they knelt on the logs and paddled slowly over to Vao.

All day the villagers stood on the beach and stared out at Vao. What if their young men were being gobbled up by **hordes** of rats? At dusk, nothing. At dawn, still nothing. That night a small black object appeared on the water. The men were returning, but not on their bamboo raft. They had carved a canoe much like the slender piece of hollow bark the rat had used to escape to Vao. Only their canoe was sturdy and long, for they had carved it from a tree.

In the days that followed, the villagers carved

hordes
  large groups, swarms

many more canoes. When there was an army of canoes, the chief launched an attack on Vao. Every rat ran to the shore, terrified of the invading warriors. They jumped onto their sticks and tried to escape.

Unlucky rats! A storm was brewing in the sky. Snarling winds and drumming rain **capsized** the rats' flimsy rafts. Every rat drowned.

The people paddled back home to Mallikolo. They held a great celebration, feasting and dancing long into the night. After that, they kept all their toes and all their taro. And every day since, they have used carved canoes to travel from island to island.

capsized
overturned

THE SEAGULL AND THE MUSSELS

It used to be that the animals of the world watched the people. By watching, they learned to behave like people, and sometimes to behave even better!

Their favorite thing to do was to watch the children. Children love to play, and the animals loved to play too. Every day they watched the children play games, like tag, or ball. When the children were taking their naps, the animals would take their turn and play and play. It was so much fun.

One day, on the island of **Gaitcha**, the children played a new game. One child covered her eyes, and the others all ran and hid. When the girl opened her eyes, everyone was out of sight. Then she ran around seeking until she found them.

"That looks like fun," said the seagull.

"Yes," agreed the mussels. "Let's play that game! You hide first. We will all cover our eyes."

The mussels all closed their shells and hid their eyes so they were not peeking. Then the seagull took off into the air to find a good place to hide.

The mussels counted to ten and began to open their shells. Far above, Seagull was still searching for a place. The sun was very bright. As Seagull flew low over the island she cast a large black shadow on the sand below.

mussels
small shellfish
with dark shells

Gaitcha
NGAY thah

129

As the shadow passed over a little baby mussel, it suddenly snapped its shell closed and squeaked, "I can see you, Seagull." By this time, that shadow had crossed over dozens of other little mussels, and they all clacked closed and shouted, "We can see you, Seagull!" They were so loud that Seagull, far above, heard them shouting.

"How did they find me?" wondered Seagull. His wings beat harder and he climbed into the sky.

The gull flew far out to sea, over the islands of **Tapout** and **We**. This time he tried to sneak in low over the beach. "They won't see me this time," he **gloated**. Just as soon as his shadow covered the first mussel, poor Seagull heard that **dreadful** cry, "We can see you, Seagull!"

Back into the sky flew Seagull. He crossed **Lovengoni** and **Dukin** and **Chepenok**. Everywhere it was the same. "We can see you, Seagull!" clacked the closing mussels when she tried to land.

Finally the exhausted gull returned to Gaitcha. "You win," she gasped. "I am too tired to keep on flying. Everywhere I go you mussels see me! I just don't know how you do it."

"Yippee!" chorused the mussels. "Now it is our turn to hide."

"Go ahead," panted Seagull. "But I warn you. I won't give up until I find you!"

Then Seagull covered her eyes with her wings and counted slowly to ten. She counted especially slowly because she was so tired. This gave the mussels time to hide (everyone knows that mussels can't run very quickly).

"Hurry," whispered the mussels. "Down to the beach. That bird won't find us here." The mussels scrambled down the beach right to the edge of the water. Then they dug halfway into the sand to hide.

(It would not be fair to dig all the way into the sand. And the mussels played fair. They didn't cheat.)

Poor Seagull. By the time she reached "ten," all of the mussels had hidden in the sand. Also by the time she reached "ten," the tide had come all the way in. Now the mussels were all under the water!

Seagull flew **aloft**. All she could see was ocean. There were no mussels anywhere. She flew back over Tapout and We and Lovengoni and Dukin and Chepenok. No mussels.

aloft
high in the air

She flew back to Gaitcha. No mussels. She flew and flew until it was getting dark. The tide was still in and she never saw a mussel.

But she didn't give up.

Even to this day you can see the seagull digging in the sand at low tide. She is making piles and piles of mussels. She does not eat the mussels. She is still looking for the mussels that first hid from her.

And even to this day if a dark shadow comes over an open mussel, it will shut with a loud "clack." The Old Ones know that this isn't just a noise. That "clack" is the mussel announcing, "I can see you, Seagull!"

THE SUN, THE MOON, AND THE WOMAN

Bonan
  MBOH nahn

Bonan, the Sun-god, wanted a wife.

Every day, as the sun majestically crossed the sky, Bonan searched the earth below for the perfect mate.

Bonan saw many women. They were attractive, but they did not meet the Sun-god's strict standards. "My wife must be perfect," he announced. "She must be beautiful to look upon, shining in my sunlight like a goddess. She must also be faithful to me, and to me alone. I am a jealous god!"

Many fathers brought their daughters to Bonan's attention. None of the young women met Bonan's standards.

orbit
  circular path

lamented
  complained

Pentecost
  PEN tuh cawst

Touyo TOW yoh

Tava TAH vah

Bonan grew discouraged, as year after year he continued his lonely **orbit** around the earth. "Will I never find a wife?" he **lamented**.

On **Pentecost** Island in New Caledonia, a mighty chief, **Touyo**, was searching for a husband for his daughter.

Touyo had many sons and daughters, but **Tava**, the youngest, was his favorite. Tava was the most beautiful woman on Pentecost Island.

Touyo searched all of the islands for a husband worthy to marry his lovely daughter. He did not find one. Suitors came and went, but none met Touyo's high standards. Tava despaired of ever finding a husband who would please her father.

"Please, father," she begged. "Look harder. I so much want to find a husband."

Touyo looked harder.

One fine day, Bonan, far up in the sky, heard the story of Tava from some birds who had just flown from Pentecost. "I must visit this island and see this beauty for myself," he vowed.

The next day, Bonan visited Touyo.

"Well, Touyo, I understand you are looking for a husband for your daughter."

"Yes, Bonan, that is true," answered Touyo. "But I cannot find any man worthy to marry one of such beauty."

"Is it true," asked Bonan, "that your Tava is the most beautiful woman on any of these islands?"

"Of course, Bonan," answered Touyo. "You must see her for yourself."

"That I would like to do," replied Bonan. "In fact, my friend, I am searching for a wife myself. Is there any chance you might consider me worthy to be a husband for your daughter?"

Touyo was overjoyed. "Of course, Bonan. I would be honored to have you as a member of my family."

"But one thing first, Touyo," said Bonan sternly. "Is your daughter's beauty matched by her **virtue**? I am a stern and jealous god. I will not tolerate any unfaithfulness in my wife."

virtue goodness

Touyo answered, a bit quickly, "Of course, Bonan. You will see. She is an island of beauty surrounded by an ocean of virtue."

Then Touyo took Bonan to see his daughter.

Tava was everything Touyo promised and more. She was the most lovely woman Bonan had ever seen. Her laughter sparkled like the sunlight on the

lagoon
shallow body of
water, often
surrounded by a
reef

captivated
charmed

courted
pursued, with
marriage as the
goal

waves, and her eyes were deeper than any **lagoon**. Bonan was **captivated**.

Tava, too, was impressed. She had never been **courted** by a god before. They were married the very next day!

After the wedding ceremony, Bonan took his new bride to their hut on the hillside. "It is getting late, my darling," announced Bonan. "I must leave you for a short time now to bring warmth and light to the other side of the earth. Wait for me and be faithful. I will be back at dawn."

Tava promised to wait. Bonan carefully closed the door to the hut. Then he rushed back into the sky to continue his earthly rounds. When Bonan returned at dawn, he opened the door to the hut. Then he spent the whole day with his new wife.

Day after day this pattern repeated. Bonan left the hut at dusk and returned at dawn. Each time he carefully closed the door to the hut when he left, and opened it quietly when he returned.

One evening, after Bonan had left, the full moon began to rise over the lagoon. Bonan's **archrival**, **Guam**, was the Moon-god. Guam had heard of Bonan's marriage. He decided to pay a visit to Bonan's new bride and see her beauty for himself.

Imagine Tava's surprise when Guam, the Moon-god, dressed in all his **finery**, knocked on the door to her hut that night!

"Hello," Guam announced. "I am a friend of your husband's. I have come to keep you company when he must be away."

Tava was confused. Bonan had not told her about this handsome stranger. "I am sorry, dear sir. My husband has told me to keep this door closed and not visit with strange men."

"Of course, my dear," answered Guam. "But

don't be silly. Your husband has wives all over the world. He is with another one right now! He is not faithful to any of these wives. Why should you be faithful to one such as this?"

None of this was true, but Guam was a good talker. Pretty soon Tava found herself opening the door to her hut and spending the whole evening with the Moon-god.

In the morning, just before dawn, Guam ran from the hut. He rushed, for he needed to continue his own travels around the earth.

The sun rose and Bonan returned to his hut. There he found the door open. Bonan knew at once what had happened.

"You were visited by my enemy, the Moon-god, weren't you?" demanded Bonan. Tava was terrified. She had never seen her husband so mad.

"And you **yielded** to his smooth talk and lies, didn't you?"

yielded gave in

Tava cried and cried. She promised Bonan she would never again be unfaithful. "Please forgive me."

Bonan looked at his wife **sternly**. "You have not kept your promise to me. I warned you that I was a jealous god. I told you I would not **tolerate** any unfaithfulness."

sternly
with displeasure

tolerate
put up with

"Now," continued the angry Bonan. "You and all women will be cursed by me. You will be punished for your unfaithfulness."

Since that day, every month, often at the time of the full moon, women have pains and bleed. This is Bonan's curse, often called the Moon-curse. It has remained with women since the time of Tava and her **seduction** by the smooth-talking Guam.

seduction
temptation

THE FIRE-WALKERS OF BEQA

Beqa
  MBENG gah

Dredre
  NDRAYN dray

Tuiqalita
  too eeng gah
  LEE tah

nabu
  NAHM boo

Long ago, a famous storyteller named **Dredre** went from village to village in Fiji. In each village he told wonderful stories. It was the custom to give Dredre fine gifts as payment for his stories.

In the village called Beqa, the chief, **Tuiqalita**, was troubled. He needed to give a fine gift, called a *nabu,* to Dredre. What would he give? Everyone else gave Dredre food or mats. Tuiqalita wanted to give something special. Something worthy of a chief! What could he choose?

Finally, he hit upon a fine idea. He remembered how Dredre LOVED to eat (he was very big). Dredre's favorite of all foods was eel. Tuiqalita would bring a great eel to Dredre for his *nabu*. All he had to do was find one.

The kind of eel he wanted lived in the ground. It was very difficult to find. Tuiqalita went all over the island digging deep holes and looking for an eel. No luck.

Namoliwai
  nah moh tee wye

Finally, in a place called **Namoliwai** he dug until the hole was deeper than a man could stand. Still he dug deeper. He had to find an eel!

Suddenly his digging opened up a dark hole. Tuiqalita was very brave, or perhaps very foolish. He stuck his whole arm into that black hole to see what he could find.

What do you suppose he found? An eel? No. He found a little man hiding in that dark hole. Tuiqalita gripped the man's arm. He pulled the man into the light where he could get a good look at him.

"Please let me go," the strange little man begged. "My name is Tui Namoliwai."

"No," said Tuiqalita, "I need a *nabu* for Dredre. YOU will be my *nabu*!"

The little man was quite afraid. He was also quite **clever**.

"If you let me go, I will give you many great warriors. You will be the MOST powerful chief."

"No," replied Tuiqalita, "I am already powerful enough. I have no need of more warriors. All that I need is a *nabu*, and you are it!"

Tui Namoliwai was even more afraid, and he **pleaded**: "If you let me go, I will give you many beautiful wives."

"No," laughed Tuiqalita, "I already have more wives than I need. Why do I want any more?"

"Well then," said the little man, "What if I give you the most marvelous power on the island? The power to resist fire."

Now Tuiqalita was curious. If he could resist fire he would be looked upon as a most remarkable chief.

"All right," he agreed. "But this better not be a trick!"

That night when Dredre finished telling his tales, all the people brought their *nabu* to the storyteller. All except Tuiqalita. The people looked at their chief.

"Build up a huge fire," he commanded. "Fill the fire pit with stones until they are red-hot."

The people did as he instructed until the pit was so hot they could barely get near. As new sticks fell on the rocks they instantly burst into flames.

clever
  quick-thinking

pleaded begged

"Watch me!" announced Tuiqalita. The people stared as Tuiqalita stood and walked slowly to the edge of the fire. No one spoke. Tuiqalita walked, barefoot, into the fire pit. The people were horrified. Their chief was walking to his death! They turned their eyes. They stuck their fingers into their ears to muffle the screams. But they didn't hear any screams. They opened their eyes. Tuiqalita, their chief, was standing in the middle of the pit, smiling and unharmed!

Dredre bowed low to Tuiqalita. "My stories tell of magic. You, Chief Tuiqalita, are magic yourself. You are indeed the greatest of all living Fijian chiefs."

To this very day on the islands of Fiji, in the village of Beqa, there are still men who have the power to walk on red-hot fire stones. No one knows how they do it. Except Tuiqalita. He knows the knowledge came from the little man under the ground, Tui Namoliwai.

WHY THE REEF STANDS FAR FROM BAU

Islands in the vast Pacific Ocean are surrounded by the not-so-peaceful Pacific. Many islands are only a few feet above the surface of the water at their highest. During times of high tide or storm they may find themselves completely **submerged**! Many are the stories told of islanders **lashing** themselves to tall palm trees to save themselves from being washed out to sea during **typhoons**.

Other islands are more **fortunate**. Some are high volcanic islands standing far above the raging surf. Still other islands have reefs that protect them from the ocean's temper.

The islands of Fiji have just such a **vast** protecting reef. It extends over three hundred miles and breaks much of the force of the open ocean before it reaches land. The reef also quiets the pounding surf. At some places, where the reef is a long way from the land, it may be hard to even hear the sound of the ocean.

The reef was not always so far from land. At one time, when the gods of the earth and sea still lived in Fiji, there lived a goddess, **Bui Vo**, on the island of Bau.

Bui Vo was hungry. Even goddesses got hungry. Bui Vo was known for her great hunger and also for her great cooking pot, which she kept near her hut.

Bau   mbow

submerged
  underwater
lashing
  tying with
  cords
typhoons
  storms with
  very strong
  winds;
  hurricanes
fortunate
  lucky
vast   very large

Bui Vo
  MBOO ee VOH

139

This cooking pot was her favorite pot. **Ivi** nuts were her favorite food.

"I am hungry," thought Bui Vo. "I will make some ivi nuts." The thought of her favorite food made Bui Vo very happy. She set to work at once.

Cooking ivi nuts is not easy. Ivi nuts are very very hard. They are too hard for even a goddess like Bui Vo to eat.

To soften the nuts, Bui Vo filled her cooking pot with water. Then she added the nuts and put the pot on a huge fire to boil. The nuts needed to boil for a very long time to make them tender.

As Bui Vo gathered wood for her fire, she did not notice a big storm approaching from the ocean. The storm began to make big waves. We call these waves "whitecaps."

Soon Bui Vo's pot was boiling well. She listened to the wonderful sound of the nuts boiling. When the boiling sound got softer, she knew it was time to add more water. She kept adding water to the pot to keep the nuts covered and boiling.

At that time, the reef around Bau was very near the shore. As the storm grew bigger, huge waves began to crash against the rocks. "Whoosh, whoosh," they cried, sounding ever so much like the "sploosh, sploosh" sound of the boiling ivi nuts.

Bui Vo heard the loud "whoosh, whoosh." "Good," she thought. "My ivi nuts are boiling well. I can almost taste them!" Bui Vo really loved ivi nuts. She relaxed in her hut and waited.

Bui Vo fell asleep. When she awoke, she remembered her nuts and started to rush out of her hut. Then she heard the familiar "whoosh, whoosh" sound. It was even louder than before. "My," she thought, "How well the ivi nuts are boiling today." Since the sound was even louder, she did not go out

to add more water to the pot.

All that day, Bui Vo rested in her hut. She kept listening for the sound of the boiling to get softer, but the loud "whoosh, whoosh" only got louder.

By this time the storm had struck the island, and rain fell all around the hut of Bui Vo. Suddenly she smelled something burning! It smelled really bad.

Bui Vo stuck her nose out of her hut and smelled to the east. It smelled bad. Then she smelled to the west. It still smelled bad. Really bad.

Bui Vo smelled out toward the ocean. She still smelled the bad smell. Then she finally smelled toward the land, toward where her ivi nuts were cooking. This time the smell was so bad she could hardly stand it.

When she looked toward the smell, she saw black smoke coming out of her cooking pot!

"My ivi nuts!" she screamed. Bui Vo rushed out of her hut. A sad sight greeted her.

The cooking pot had boiled completely dry. Inside her favorite pot was a smoking black mess. The ivi nuts had burned to charcoal. "My ivi nuts are burned! I do not have any supper," she wailed. But that was not all.

While Bui Vo looked into her pot, the large earthenware pot suddenly cracked into two pieces. The **ruined** pot lay in the ashes of the fire. "My pot! My favorite pot is ruined."

ruined
damaged beyond repair

At first Bui Vo was sad. Then she was mad. "Why did this happen?" she demanded. Then she heard the "whoosh, whoosh" of the waves striking the reef. Bui Vo understood.

"You tricked me!" she screamed at the reef. "You and your waves sounded like my boiling pot of ivi nuts. You are a wicked reef. Go away. Go far away from this place."

The reef obeyed. Now the reef is built far out to sea. The sounds of the surf can no longer be heard on Bau.

POLYNESIA

Polynesia is the largest of the three Pacific regions of Micronesia, Melanesia, and Polynesia. This **vast** "triangle" extends from the Hawaiian Islands in the north to New Zealand in the southwest and then to lonely Easter Island in the far east. Despite this enormous size, the people, languages, and customs are very similar throughout the region. Although Polynesians may live thousands of miles apart, they can often understand one another. In contrast, Micronesia has hundreds of different languages, and Melanesia has thousands.

The reason for this similarity is that the early settlers of Polynesia came from the same areas. The islands of Polynesia were the last in the Pacific to be settled. In fact New Zealand, Hawai'i, and the Society Islands (in French Polynesia) were among the last **habitable** places on earth to be populated.

The first waves of settlement into Polynesia began almost four thousand years ago. **Voyagers** came from Melanesia to Tonga and the Samoas. The

vast   very large

habitable
able to be lived in

voyagers
people who travel by sea

Marquesas Islands (in French Polynesia) were reached only one thousand years ago. From there, settlement fanned out to the Cook Islands and to Hawai'i. Last came "The Great Migration" to New Zealand, only 750 years ago.

Before European contact, Polynesian cultures built complex societies. An important idea in these cultures was *mana*. This was the power present in all persons and objects. Persons with great amounts of *mana,* such as chiefs, were respected, often worshipped. Commoners, those with less *mana,* were not allowed to touch even the shadow of a chief. Chiefs held total power over their people. If a chief ordered someone's death, that person was quickly killed. The legends "Turtle and Shark" and "Chief's Day Ends" describe how the courage of a few people—even one young boy—helped change this tradition. But even today, in many places, it is not right to step over a person's legs, or to stand with one's head above that of a person of high rank. These actions could all lessen a person's *mana*.

The arrival of Europeans changed these islands. At first, explorers just visited. Later, missionaries and traders came to stay. Sandalwood was an important export until it ran out. Many of the islands were raided for slaves. Europeans brought diseases and guns. Some island populations were almost wiped out by diseases brought by the ships: measles, **venereal** diseases, smallpox. The missionaries became advisors to the local rulers. At times they acted as go-betweens for receiving weapons and other help from European powers.

venereal
sexually
transmitted

By the end of the 1800s, England, Germany, France, and the United States, the "Big Powers" of the world, had divided the islands of Polynesia among themselves.

The French established protectorates (mostly protecting the islands from the English) over what is now French Polynesia and later over Wallis and Futuna. The English controlled Tonga and the Cook Islands. Germany annexed Samoa. The United States took Hawai'i.

International events, particularly the World Wars and the Great Depression, brought even more changes. Germany lost all her Pacific holdings when she lost the war. The United States took American Samoa. New Zealand took Western Samoa.

After World War II, opposition to **colonialism** arose all over the Pacific. New Zealand granted independence to Western Samoa in 1962. Tonga became an independent kingdom, but was still a member of the British Commonwealth. Other nation-states were born, some with new names. The history and fortunes of Polynesia, like its tides, continued to rise and fall.

colonialism
settlement and control by a distant country

Today, these islands find themselves again at a crossroads. Much of their traditional culture has been lost. Too many of the islands depend on government jobs or foreign money. The islands are too small to have much of a political voice. They have tried to band together to get a larger voice. But traditional differences between these islands make having a single voice difficult. There are many challenges.

AMERICAN SAMOA

The Samoas were settled almost four thousand years ago, probably from Tonga. From Samoa, settlers spread out farther east to the rest of Polynesia.

American Samoa is a territory of the United States. Its six islands are politically separate from Samoa (which used to be called Western Samoa), although their cultures and history were united before European contact. Five of the six islands are close together. The sixth, Swain's Island, lies almost three hundred miles north. Swain's is actually part of a different group of islands. This island is privately owned. The owner, an American, wanted to be part of the U.S. territory.

The main island, **Tutuila**, is peaked, lush, and rainy. **Anthropologist** Margaret Mead thought it looked like "crushed green velvet." Waterfalls cascade from cloud-covered peaks. The deep natural harbor in **Pago Pago** is what first attracted the attention of the United States Navy.

Samoan life is called the *fa'a Samoa.* Villages are ruled by an elected chief, the *matai.* The matai titles are very important. They are often given as great gifts, or fought over in court.

Another big influence in Samoa is the church. Many Samoans spend all day Sunday at church, or quietly at their homes, called *fale.* It is against the rules in villages to swim or play loud music on Sunday.

The third big influence is the government. The U.S. government is the biggest employer in Samoa. Tuna canneries were big employers until recently. Many have moved to other islands.

SAMOA

Samoa consists of nine islands in the western part of the Samoan Islands. The eastern part makes up American Samoa. These islands were all formed by volcanic activity. The most recent volcanic **eruption** was in 1911 on the large island of **Savai'i**.

Samoa was the first of the former "Trust Territories" to achieve independence, in 1962. Until 1998, it was called Western Samoa.

Tutuila
too too EE lah

anthropologist
scientist who studies people and their cultures

Pago Pago
pahng oh pahng oh

fa'a Samoa
fah ah SAH moh ah

matai
mah TAH ee

fale   FAH leh

eruption
outpouring of lava

Savai'i
sah vah EE ee

146

Samoans are much more traditional, but much poorer, than American Samoans. Their *fale* are often built in the traditional manner, with thatched roofs, open sides, and a coral foundation. Newer concrete and tin-roofed structures are becoming more common. Traditional dancing and the authority of the chiefs, the *matai*, remain important. Agriculture and tourism are both important in the economy.

Samoans are big people, some of the biggest in the Pacific. The men often decorate their bodies with beautiful tattoos. These tattoos cover almost the whole body. Getting tattooed can be very painful. A completed tattoo is seen as a sign of honor and courage.

Samoa was briefly a colony of Germany. After Germany lost World War I, control was transferred to New Zealand. In 1962, Samoa became the first independent Polynesian state. It voted to join the British Commonwealth.

TUVALU

Tuvalu means "Eight Standing Together." Tuvalu is a string of nine low coral atolls. But only eight of these atolls have people living on them. These islands were called the Ellice Islands before they became independent members of the British Commonwealth in 1978.

About ten thousand people live on these islands. As on many other islands, there are few jobs for the islanders. Tourism and fishing are important.

TOKELAU

These three small atolls were also a part of England's Gilbert and Ellice islands. Now they are a dependency of New Zealand. Swain's Island, now part of American Samoa, was originally part of the

Tokelau group.

Because it is so small, Tokelau depends on New Zealand for many services. Tokelau has no high schools, cities, airport, or port. **Copra** is the only export.

The humorous tale "How Counting Came to Tokelau" tells how tiny creatures, working together, rewarded a young boy for his unselfishness and bravery. This small boy, with the help of an old man's magic, outwits a fierce cannibal.

NIUE

Niue is a single isolated island almost midway between Tonga and the Cook Islands. It has no close neighbors. It is self-governing in free association with New Zealand.

Tourism and agriculture are important. Much of the money needed for the government comes from New Zealand. In the past, **blackbirders** took almost all the men from Niue.

COOK ISLANDS

These fifteen tiny islands are a self-governing state in free association with New Zealand. The largest island, Rarotonga, is only four miles wide. These islands were all formed from the peaks of undersea volcanoes. They are steep, with tall mountains. The story of Rori, who hid in these mountains for years, is told in "Rori-of-the-Rocks."

As in other island nations in Polynesia, the government is the biggest employer. Tourism is also a big business, particularly from New Zealand. Precious black pearls are also a growing business.

The earliest settlers came from French Polynesia. The English arrived with Captain James Cook. Missionaries from London soon followed. These missionaries had a strong influence on the government.

In 1888 the British annexed the islands to prevent the French from taking over, as they had in Tahiti. Later, the islands were annexed by New Zealand. In 1965 the Cook Islands became self-governing.

TONGA

Tonga is relatively large compared with many other island nations. It consists of over 160 islands and atolls. On the larger islands the soil is fertile, and excellent crops are grown. Tonga has many kinds of plants and birds. Agriculture is the main source of income.

Tongans are some of the biggest people in the whole world. Being big is considered a sign of wealth and importance. Tapa cloth is another sign of wealth. Tapa is made from the pounded bark of the mulberry tree and decorated with natural dyes.

Legends report and scientists agree that Tongans settled their islands only about three thousand years ago. Their legends do not mention migration. They say that the gods **Māui** and **Tangaloa** created the islands and the people. One creation story says that the young **demigod** Māui went fishing in the ocean one day and hooked a string of islands. Māui boasted that he could pull them all up. Indeed he did. In another fishing story, Tangaloa used a magic turtle hook he found in Samoa. With this hook, he fished up Tonga. You can read two stories about Tangaloa in "The Creation of the Tongan Islands, People, and Kings."

In 1900, the British established a protectorate over Tonga (protecting it from the Germans). Tonga became an independent country in 1970, but it is a member of the British Commonwealth. Tonga also has a king, Tupou IV.

Māui   MAH oo i

Tangaloa tahn gah LOH ah

demigod a being with more power than a human but less power than a god

149

PITCAIRN ISLAND

Pitcairn Island is one of the smallest, most isolated, and yet most well known of all the islands in the Pacific. It is only one mile long and two miles wide. No more than two hundred people can live there or the island becomes too crowded. On the other hand, if the island has too few people, there may not be enough people to do all the work. This is one of Pitcairn's major problems.

Pitcairn was first settled long ago. These now-forgotten Polynesians carved huge stone statues like those found on Easter Island. Then they left. Pitcairn is famous because it became the refuge of the mutineers from the *Bounty*. This **mutiny**, in 1789, has been the subject of many books and movies. Most of the people living there are descendants of those mutineers and their Tahitian wives. Others are descendants of English and American sailors who came in the early 1800s.

NORFOLK ISLAND

Norfolk Island lies at the opposite end of Polynesia from Pitcairn Island, between New Zealand and New Caledonia.

The original inhabitants are long forgotten. Norfolk was used as a prison island by England in the early 1800s. When the population of distant Pitcairn Island grew too large, the people were all moved to Norfolk, a bigger island. Today, most of the inhabitants of Norfolk are Pitcairn descendants.

Norfolk is economically much healthier than much of Polynesia. Tourism is important. Norfolk, the original source of the world-famous Norfolk pine trees, is a territory of Australia.

WALLIS AND FUTUNA

This strangely named place is actually two different island groups lying 125 miles apart. The larger, Wallis, was named after Captain Samuel Wallis, an Englishman who first "found" these islands. Wallis is traditionally called **Uvea**.

Both of these islands are steep volcanic islands. They have excellent fresh water but little land available for agriculture.

Most of the people live on Uvea, or Wallis. This island is better developed, but there are very few natural resources.

Wallis and Futuna are administered as an overseas territory of France. Early French missionaries petitioned for French protection from the British. The islands were officially annexed in 1887.

FRENCH POLYNESIA

French Polynesia includes 130 islands in five island groups. The Society Islands, including **Tahiti, Moorea**, and **Bora-Bora,** are the largest and most developed. These beautiful islands have tall cloud-covered peaks and sparkling **lagoons**.

The Tuamotu **Archipelago** lies just west of the Society Islands. These are low coral islands with large lagoons, pearls, and many fish. The Tuamotus are also the site of the French nuclear bomb testing.

The other three island groups—the Austral Islands, the Marquesas group, and **Mangareva**—are much less developed.

The economy of French Polynesia is based on tourism. It is also helped by the presence of the French military supporting the nuclear bomb testing. French Polynesia is an overseas territory of France.

Settlement began in the Marquesas some two

Tahiti
tah HEE tee

Moorea
moh uh RAY uh

Bora-Bora
boh rah boh rah

lagoon
shallow body of water, often surrounded by a reef or an atoll

archipelago
group of islands

Mangareva
mahng ah RAY vah

thousand years ago. From the Marquesas, the Society Islands were settled.

The French annexed Tahiti as a **protectorate** in 1842. In recent years, as in much of Polynesia, pressures for local self-government have grown. In 1963 the French began nuclear bomb testing in the Tuamotus. Worldwide criticism forced them to move this testing underground in 1975. Criticism increased even further when the French secret service blew up the *Rainbow Warrior.* This was a **yacht** involved in protests against nuclear testing in the Pacific.

EASTER ISLAND

Easter Island is the only Polynesian island controlled by a South American power, Chile. Easter Island lies far from any other island. It is over one thousand miles from its nearest neighbor, Pitcairn Island.

To the original inhabitants, this was *Rapa Nui* (Great Rapa) or *Te Pito te Henua* (Navel of the World). It was named Easter Island by early Dutch explorers. They landed there on Easter Sunday.

A population of three thousand was reduced by disease and slave raids. By 1877, only 111 people were left. Because the island is very small and very isolated, few plants or animals naturally **thrive** there. "Makemake and the Birds of Easter Island" describes the problems a shortage of food can cause.

More than six hundred huge stone statues dot the island. Some are over one thousand years old. Little is known of their builders.

protectorate
an island or island group protected by a more powerful country

yacht
small ship

Rapa Nui
rah pah NOO ee

Te Pito te Henua
teh pee toh teh heh NOO ah

thrive
grow well

HAWAIIAN ISLANDS

Hawai'i is the largest and most developed island group in Polynesia. These were among the last islands settled in the entire Pacific. They are also the youngest geologically. Active volcanoes, like Kīlauea on Hawai'i, the "Big Island," are still changing the landscape. The seven inhabited Hawaiian islands are Kaua'i, Ni'ihau, O'ahu, Maui, Moloka'i, Lāna'i, and Hawai'i.

The first Hawaiians probably came from French Polynesia. Each island had its own king. All were united under Kamehameha I by 1795. This united kingdom was overthrown by U.S.-backed sugar planters. Hawai'i was **annexed** as a U.S. Territory. It later became the fiftieth state of the United States.

annexed added on

Today, Hawai'i has over one million people. Most are a mix of Europeans, Japanese, Chinese, and many other Asians and Pacific Islanders. Few are "pure" Hawaiians. Most of the original Hawaiian people died of disease brought by whalers, missionaries, and other settlers.

Economically, Hawai'i depends on agriculture, tourism, and the U.S. military. In recent years, with the decline in all these sources of income, the people have had a difficult time. This lower income, together with a very high cost of living, creates challenges for even these well-developed islands.

NEW ZEALAND

New Zealand lies at the southwest corner of the "Polynesian Triangle." It has two main islands, called North Island and South Island. These are the only islands in Polynesia to lie outside the tropics. The first settlers to New Zealand came from "**Hawaiki**." This was probably in French Polynesia.

Hawaiki
hah vah EE kee

With 10,000-foot snow-capped mountains, New Zealand must have been quite a shock to these first migrants.

The original settlers became the **Maori** people. They call these islands "**Aotearoa**." The Maori can still trace their ancestors back almost one thousand years. Villagers point with pride to the names of the sailing canoes that brought their ancestors in "The Great Migration." This migration occurred in about the year 1250, only 750 years ago. No one is certain why the Maori made such a long and difficult move. There was much fighting and cannibalism in Polynesia at that time. Perhaps this is why they left.

New Zealand lies over one thousand miles from its nearest neighbor, Australia. New Zealand became independent in 1947. It was once a British colony. Now it is a member of the British Commonwealth. Many settlers from Britain moved to New Zealand. They now outnumber the original Maori.

CHIEF'S DAY ENDS

"**C**hief's Day!" was announced.

The young prince did not understand. His friends hid all day in fear. Why were they afraid on Chief's Day? They wouldn't come out to throw the fishing nets. They refused to race up the coconut palms and be the one to throw down the most coconuts. They wouldn't swim in the royal ponds. Instead they stayed hidden until the king's Chief's Day **feast** was finished.

This young prince, **Polua-le-uli-gana**—a royal name shortened to Prince Polua until he became the king—was sad. He didn't understand why on Chief's Day his playmates stayed in hiding, or why one of them would never be seen again. When the prince questioned a servant, he got no answer. The servant simply walked away.

Prince Polua lived with his royal Samoan family at **Tualagi**, a large village inland from the sea. On one side was the area of **Afaga,** and on the other side was **Malie**. Many paths led toward this royal village. Many people walked these paths to bring gifts, food, news, and greetings to the prince's father, King **Malietoa Liulamatutu**. Some people came because they were commanded—some to be honored, some to be punished.

The prince was tired of all the noise and confusion.

feast
    meal often accompanied by celebration or entertainment

Polua-le-uli-gana
poh LOO ah leh OO lee NGAH nah

Tualagi
too ah LAH ngee

Afaga
ah FAH ngah

Malie
mah LEE eh

Malietoa Liulamatutu
mah lee eh TOH ah lee oo lah mah TOO too

He was lonely. Tomorrow had been declared Chief's Day. As usual, all of his friends were hiding. People hurried from **task** to task with worried looks and sad glances. The Prince felt as if they were preparing for a funeral rather than for a feast day.

He walked a long distance from his home. Finally, just as the sun was falling behind the sea, the prince reached **Fatitu**. This was his favorite place, a place to see everything but not be seen. He climbed up the steep cliff until he reached his "watching rock," a large flat rock that stuck out from the cliff. Here he could see the sky above, the ocean beyond, and the **meandering** pathway below. The prince rested.

It was night when voices woke him. The moon was full. The silver of its shining face flowed across the sea's wrinkled surface like a ghostly path. The prince shivered. The rock beneath him was still warm from the day's heat. But the dark night all around him felt shivery with danger. The voices that were once far away were now directly below him. The prince listened.

"If you could have one wish before you die, what would it be?" The voice was young, a child's voice, perhaps the voice of someone his own age.

"I would paddle out beyond the reef and watch the frigate birds fish the open sea. Oh how I would like to glide on the winds higher and higher and then plunge straight down to spear a fat, juicy fish. I'd swallow it whole. With a full belly I'd glide again round and round, closing my eyes and **dozing** in the sunshine."

"How can you talk of food when tomorrow is Chief's Day?"

"Stop! Tonight I will not think about tomorrow. Until the sun rises, we are alive. So let us live!"

task
  chore, small job

Fatitu
  fah TEE too

meandering
  winding

dozing
  sleeping, napping

156

"I cannot stop thinking about the horror of tomorrow. I don't want to die! I don't want to be eaten!" There were no more words, only one voice crying and the other trying to comfort.

Suddenly the prince understood. His legs began to tremble, his stomach heaved, and his heart pounded madly with pain. On every Chief's Day one of his friends disappeared. On every Chief's Day a feast was prepared for his father. Lesser chiefs from all around the kingdom of Samoa came to share the feast. A special animal was roasted. His father was always given the tender **nape** of the neck and the sweet juicy heart. Now the prince realized. "The animal I thought was a roasted pig was a child, a boy like me! That is why my friends hid. That is why no one answered my questions. Somehow I must put an end to this murderous feasting on Chief's Day!"

nape back

The prince shouted out. "Brave travelers, listen! Please wait. I must speak with you!"

Suddenly the sounds of the night stopped. Silence filled the darkness and seemed to echo in Polua's ears. "I am the king's own son, Polua-le-uli-gana. I will not harm you. Who are you? Tell me the story of your journey."

At first the two young travelers said nothing. The prince shouted again, "Speak to me. Perhaps I can save your lives."

One of the young men whispered to the other. "We have nothing to lose. We might die now if this is some wicked trick. So what? Tomorrow we die in the king's kitchen."

One of the young men called out, "We are from **Savai'i**. We were selected from the *matai*'s family. Tomorrow we finish our journey. Tomorrow we meet our death with courage that will honor our family."

Savai'i
sah vah EE ee

matai
(mah tah ee) chief'

The prince listened. As he listened his heart nearly broke with sorrow. And then a plan began to form. A dangerous plan. He might lose his life. But he might gain life for many others.

The prince stepped forward and gave a strange order. "Climb this coconut tree that stands between shore and sea. Break off its finest branch. Hurry. Already the sky loses its darkness with the nearness of day."

The two young men ran to the tree. Within minutes they returned with a large palm **frond**.

frond leaf

plait
    braid, weave

"**Plait** the palm into a mat. Wait. Let me lie in the middle of it."

Again they obeyed, wrapping the prince in the middle of the palm frond as if he were a freshly caught fish.

"Good. I am ready." The prince's voice was stern and clear. "Carry me to the king. Hurry. I hear the roosters warning that night has ended."

The two men carried their bundle to the king. With heads bowed to the ground, they placed the wrapped bundle at the king's feet.

King Malietoa called to his chiefs. "Here is a fine catch brought for our feast. Prepare it as usual. Once it is roasted, invite all to join me as I cut out the heart and eat the neck. The rest you all can share."

The royal cooks opened the bundle. They gasped in horror. Quickly they fell to their knees.

The king roared. "Why this disobedience? Shall

I have you thrown into the fire with the fish?"

"Look for yourself. It is not a fish. It is your own son, our royal Prince Polua-le-uli-gana!"

The king's face **paled**. He stared at his beloved son. The prince continued to sit, head bowed, not saying a word, waiting for a killing blow. But the blow did not happen. The prince looked up at his father. Only then did the father understand the sorrow and **anguish** he had so many times caused.

The king looked at the bowed heads, waiting in perfect silence for his next command. "Rejoice!" he said. "Let this day begin a new feast, a new celebration. My son has risked his life so I might see. The eating of children ends this very day!" The king turned to his chiefs. "Fish shall be used to celebrate Chief's Day. Fish, chicken, and tasty plump pigs will be feast foods for all sacred days!"

The great King Malietoa kept his word. Of course, so did his sons and grandsons after him. Thus it is told and retold, that because of the brave and loving act of Prince Polua-le-uli-gana, cannibalism ended in Samoa.

paled
turned white

anguish
deep pain or great suffering

SAMOA

TURTLE AND SHARK

Within the telling of this legend is the telling of another. Some people think legends are made-up stories that have little value except for entertainment. Maybe those people are afraid to look closely at things they can't explain. Other people think legends contain important truths. These truths are not found in scientific research. These truths are seen in the wisdom within every culture's traditions and beliefs. We each decide what kind of truth we want to see or believe.

Vaitongi
vah ee TONG ee

*If you stand on the sea cliffs at **Vaitongi**, you will see an unexplainable truth. If you believe in what is told but cannot be proven, you will see the turtle and the shark. They are a very unlikely pair. Why would they swim to the surface at such an unlikely place? Samoans say that you will see nothing unless you believe.*

Letuli
leh TOO lee

*Before you walk to the cliff's edge, invite a few children of the **Letuli** clan to stand with you. Ask them to sing the words that invite first the turtle and then the shark. The children will teach you the song.*

Stand very still. Concentrate very hard. Look seaward and repeat over and over the chanting song that invites and welcomes the pair. Shout the ending words that sound like a war whoop, "Choo—hoo hoo!" Of course the turtle will not instantly pop up.

160

Be patient. Sing with your soul. Believe in your heart. And watch. You will see them.

*At first you will see the turtle, her round orange-yellow shell coming slowly toward the surface. Sing louder. Greet her. Join in with the children's excited calls, "***Lalelei****! Lalelei! Beautiful!"*

Look again. You will see the shark's dark fin slicing through the crashing waves. Lalelei! Yes, it is true. I have read the words of others telling of it. I myself have sung to the turtle, and she came.

King **Malietoa Faiga** had long been king of the great Samoan island of **'Upolu**. This king was known for his cruelty. He was especially known for his enormous appetite for human flesh. Whomever he took a liking to eat, he ate. No one could argue or **protest**. No High Court could declare the choice illegal. If someone's name was called to be supper, that unlucky person was supper.

On the far south side of the distant island of **Savai'i**, there lived a man and his wife, **Fonuea**. Their **devotion** to each other was well known. They lived a simple life. The husband fished their food from the sea. **Obedient** to the ways of their people, he gave the best and biggest fish to the village chief. The wife wove the finest of mats. Without complaining she shared her time and talent with the village women. Fonuea and her husband asked for little. They gave with pleasure. But their contentment was soon shattered.

The King heard of their happiness. He desired to taste such happy hearts. "Would be quite good for my aching stomach. Might help get rid of this gas. A husband with a heart of joy. Just what I need to eat!"

He sent a messenger by sea. "Race across the waves with full sail. Hurry to Savai'i!"

lalelei
lah leh LEH ee

Malietoa Faiga
mah lee eh toh ah fah EE ngah

'Upolu
oo POH loo

protest
  complain, object

Savai'i
Sah vah EE ee

Fonuea
foh noo EH ah

devotion
  faithful love

obedient
  doing as one is told

outrigger
> sailing canoe
> with a long thin
> float attached
> alongside

fale FAH leh

The messenger did not rest, not even to sleep or eat, until his **outrigger** reached Savai'i. Once on land he raced to a distant village. There he brought his command of horror to the quiet home, the *fale*, of Fonuea and her husband.

Fonuea fell to her knees and begged her husband, "Let us escape. We can sail away. Go somewhere, anywhere, to another island and hide forever if we need to."

Her husband sadly shook his head. "No, my dearest Fonuea. If we do not obey, the king will punish everyone in this village. Even the children. If he has decided to eat my heart, he must have it." Then he looked into Fonuea's dark dark eyes and swallowed back his sadness. "I have been chosen to die. You must live for us both. Fill each day with joy for both of us."

Fonuea wrapped her arms around her husband's legs. "If you will not run away with me, then at least let me travel with you to 'Upolu. One more day, one more day, it can be an entire lifetime." And so he agreed.

typhoon
> storm with very
> strong winds;
> hurricane

catchment
> something that
> collects
> rainwater

pandanus
> plant fiber used
> for weaving
> mats, baskets,
> and other
> products

Tutuila
too too EE lah

Iliili
ee lee EE lee

They set out from Savai'i in their small outrigger canoe. The messenger followed closely in his. As they were nearing the royal residence on 'Upolu, a sudden storm whipped up enormous waves. A strange silent wind with the force of a **typhoon** blew their outrigger far out to sea. For many days they drifted in an unknown ocean. They celebrated each new day they could share. Fonuea made a **catchment** from the torn **pandanus** sail. She was calm and steady as a turtle. Her husband hunted food from the sea. He was swift as a shark, providing plenty of fish.

Finally, their little outrigger drifted to a distant island, **Tutuila**. Here the chief, **Letuli** of **Iliili**, was kind and welcoming. The couple presented themselves at the king's royal *fale* and told their story. The chief remembered how Tutuila was once a place where chiefs ate the sons of brothers. But no more. Certainly this was a sign that people were meant to be good friends and neighbors, not meals, for each other.

"You are welcome. Your safe arrival is a sign of blessing. The gods are happy. We are happy. Here you can have a safe home for as long as you wish."

Fonuea and her husband wept with joy. For many years they lived on Tutuila in the village of Vaitongi. Each day before dawn they gave thanks for having one more day together. Often they asked, "What can we do to thank the king as generously as he has given?" One morning as they watched the surf crashing and tumbling, they looked at each other. They looked again at the foamy sea. Both nodded. They knew what would be a fitting gift.

The two went directly to the king at his *fale*. He had been expecting them. Kneeling, they bowed until their foreheads touched the ground.

Fonuea spoke. "Royal and wise, most gentle King Letuli of Iliili, forgive our **haste**. Please walk with us to cliff's edge at Vaitongi. We wish to present a gift to you that will make your kindness famous. The mystery of this gift will be told from one to another, from old to young again and again. In its telling, people will remember the value of kindness and caring for one another."

haste   hurry

The chief did not know what to say. He thought they would be asking to return to their own village on Savai'i. "Have you not heard?" he asked them. "King Malietoa this day declared **cannibalism taboo**! His own son wrapped himself in a coconut **frond** and had himself brought as an offering to his

cannibalism
the eating of human flesh by other humans

taboo
forbidden, not allowed

frond   leaf

cruel father. Imagine such daring! The king realized the horror of his selfish appetite!" The chief smiled at the two bowed heads. "My kind visitors. Your behavior has been a great inspiration to my people. That is gift enough. You can return home safely. I will give you one of my royal canoes."

The aged husband of Fonuea slowly stood up. He shook his head. "Thank you, great chief. Allow us to give you what little we have. Receive our gift of story. It will be told and retold. Generations will remember the horror of flesh-eating. They will also remember the power of kindness."

The chief nodded. "So it will be."

Fonuea and her husband walked the winding path to Vaitongi. The chief led the way. As villagers saw the unusual **procession** they became curious. Many joined in. Children pointed and called out. Fonuea called to them all. "Come. Come and see. Stand with us. Sing with us." Soon the laughing and **clamoring** of children became as noisy and **raucous** as the wild surf itself.

And then a great silence hung uneasily over the crowd. Even the shrill calling of **terns** and **boobies ceased**. Children **thronged** around the chief, Fonuea, and her husband. The chief nodded. Fonuea and her husband stepped forward to the very edge of the cliff. They joined hands. One glance backward. One last smile to each other. And then they stepped off the cliff.

Their bodies were smashed against the dark rock far below. But no blood reddened the waters. Fonuea's black hair swirled around and around, making a circle. The light of the sun seemed to glow from within it. And then, it was no longer a circle. Clearly all could see the back of a turtle.

No one said a word. Villagers looked at each

procession
> group of people moving in an orderly, often ceremonial, way

clamoring
> shouting

raucous
> harsh and disorderly

terns
> small seabirds

boobies
> large seabirds

ceased stopped

thronged
> crowded together

other, afraid to admit what they had witnessed. And then a child pointed, shouting. "Look! A shark. The fin of a shark. He follows the turtle."

Indeed, the shark did swim toward the turtle. The dark head of the turtle lifted out of the water, looked at the children, hesitated, and then dipped below the swirling waves. The turtle's golden-brown shell **hovered** at the surface and then disappeared.

This time it was the booming voice of the chief that spoke. "Listen. I hear singing coming from the crashing surf."

Once again the people hushed. This time the shark swam toward the shore and then plunged into the surf. The foam crackled and whooshed. Some say that words could be heard.

Children, sing for our return and we will come. Remember the reason for our gift. Sing to us with joy and **compassion***.*

hovered
    stayed at one
    spot

compassion
    concern for the
    suffering of
    others

RESCUE WITH FRUIT BATS

Leutogi
leh oo TOH ngee

"**D**on't touch it!"

"I have to. Maybe it's dying. See, it's barely breathing." **Leutogi**, the princess from Samoa, reached for the little brown creature lying under a rock. "It's a baby bat, a flying fox. If I don't help it, it will die." The bat was no bigger than a kitten, but furry like a fox. Its big brown eyes looked up at the princess.

"Let it die!" The king's servant frowned and grunted in disapproval. "Stupid Samoan girl. No Tongan would touch a flying fox, especially a sick one."

Leutogitupa'tea
leh oo toh ngee
too pah TEH ah

betrothed
engaged to be married

Tuitoga
too ee TOH ngah

archenemy
main enemy

glanced
looked quickly

glared
stared angrily

Leutogi was a princess from Samoa. Her full royal name was **Leutogitupa'tea**. She was **betrothed** to the King of Tonga. She was to be his second wife. King **Tuitoga** did not like her prowling the jungles instead of behaving like a proper Tongan wife-to-be. A royal princess should spend her time quietly weaving fine mats or carefully combing the royal hair of the queen. The king had arranged this marriage to make peace with Tonga's **archenemy**, Samoa. Unfortunately, these neighboring island nations remained at war. Samoans and Tongans fiercely disliked and distrusted each other.

Leutogi **glanced** over her shoulder and **glared** back at the servant. She knew that as soon as they returned to the royal village, the servant would tell the queen about the flying fox. The queen would tell the king, and once again, the entire royal court of Tonga would make fun of her. Leutogi, the princess from Samoa, engaged to be the second wife of King Tuitoga, would be **ridiculed** for taking pity on an ugly injured bat.

The little creature trembled as it tried to hide farther beneath the rock. Leutogi reached down. "You poor thing. I just want to help you. I know how it feels to be scared and have no one who cares."

"Don't touch it!" reminded the servant. "One bite from a **vile** creature like a flying fox can make you go crazy!" The sharp scolding scared both the princess and the bat. The little creature scratched frantically, trying to hide. And then he tried to fly.

"Look! Such **frail** wings, and one is broken. Oh, no, it will injure itself worse with all that scratching and flapping. Hush, little one. I won't hurt you, hush." Leutogi reached toward the terrified animal. She curled her hand around its back, carefully folding its winged arms against its body.

"Flying foxes—bats—phew!" The servant spat on the injured bat. "An animal that flies when it was meant to walk—phew—an evil animal good for only one thing, being eaten. Bat wings boiled in coconut cream, delicious! But a sickly one like this will cause trouble. Let it go, foolish princess. Let the rats eat it. Let them become crazed with its evil black blood!"

But Leutogi ignored the warning. She snapped off a soft, curled leaf from a banana tree and wrapped it around the trembling creature. *Let them tease all they want. Maybe I can give comfort to something that is also scared and alone.*

Leutogi hid the bat in her hut. But every morning

summoned
commanded to appear

pandanus
plant fiber used for weaving mats, baskets, and other products

ravenously
with great eagerness

when she was **summoned** to wait on the king's first wife, all the servants teased, flapping their arms and chirping like bats.

At every meal Leutogi sat alone on her **pandanus** mat. She saved bits of papaya, mango, and guava—food for the little bat. In the darkness of the night, she sat outside her hut feeding the flying fox in her lap. She looked north toward her own island and softly chanted stories to her little friend.

The flying fox ate **ravenously**. Quickly its broken wing healed. Leutogi knew it was time to set it free. She held the little bat and stroked its pointed nose. It stared up at her with big round eyes, its ears turned toward her face as if it were waiting for her to begin chanting.

"Tonight there will be no stories. You are ready to return to the forest and find your own food." Leutogi waited until the torches were put out, the cooking fires had become glowing embers, the women were sleeping, and the men had retreated to the men's house to argue long into the night about village politics. Leutogi peered into the darkness and stepped out.

She hurried toward the ocean, stood on the edge of a volcanic ledge, extended her hand high up to the starry sky, and uncurled her fingers. "Fly away, little one. Fly to your freedom."

With a quiet whoosh of its wings, the flying fox flew away.

The next morning, Leutogi was given a new responsibility. The queen's son was no longer a baby, so Leutogi, as second wife, was commanded to care for the child, day and night, exactly as the queen ordered.

The child was spoiled and demanding. The queen was impossible to please. The entire day

Leutogi was busy **fetching** this, getting that, or carrying the boy to a new place of amusement. The only time Leutogi could escape was during the forbidden secrecy of night. Once the child was asleep, she hurried toward the ocean and sat hidden under the thick branches of a breadfruit tree. She gazed north, greeted the familiar stars, and chanted softly in Samoan. The sounds and words of her own language were her only comfort.

Suddenly she felt the presence of something or someone near. She could not see, but she could hear breathing. "Who are you? Want do you want?"

A whoosh of air answered her question. "Flying fox! I have missed you so much! Come closer. I will tell you a story."

From that night on, Leutogi would slip away from her hut once the child was asleep. Bringing handfuls of fruit, she'd sit quietly under the bread-fruit tree and wait for her winged friend. Soon other bats came too. Dozens and dozens swooped out of the velvet blackness. Upside-down they hung along every branch of the tree. She chanted her stories and fed them sweet pieces of papaya. She was not afraid of their winged arms or hook-like fingers. Soon the bats were not afraid of her.

One night as she hurried back toward the village, she heard shouting and screaming. Torches were lit. People were running from all directions toward her hut. What could be wrong? What could have happened? And then she heard the queen herself scream into the darkness. *The king's son was dead.* Leutogi would be held responsible. She was never, ever to have left his side!

Leutogi was sentenced to die. She was dragged to the **outskirts** of the village and tied to a tree. Wood was heaped around her. Everyone—men, women,

fetching
  getting and
  bringing back

outskirts
  part away from
  the center

169

and children—was ordered to watch and remember. Children stood silently beside their mothers. Only one brave voice was heard. Leutogi was chanting, her voice calm and steady. The king roared a command. The royal servants marched forward carrying blazing torches.

The fire was lit. Everyone ran from the flames, expecting to hear terrible screams of death. But they heard nothing. They shivered in the unexpected quiet and then looked up. Winged shadows darkened the sky.

Swarm after swarm of bats flew over the flames, urinating. The children laughed. They held their noses and ran back to the tree where Leutogi was tied. The fire was out. The bats had drenched the flames!

The king was enraged. He roared that if Leutogi couldn't be killed by fire, then she would be starved to death. She was tied onto an outrigger canoe and paddled to a deserted island. On this volcanic point of barren rock, nothing grew and no water flowed.

Every day the king's servant paddled out to see if Leutogi was dead. But every day he found her happy and content—not one bit hungry or thirsty. Disgusted, he spat in front of her. Leutogi returned his rude greeting with respectful Samoan words. Then she held out her hand to offer a choice piece of papaya.

The servant spat again and screamed, "You must be part demon! Where did you find food on this dead island?"

Leutogi smiled and pointed to the empty sky. Once again she offered to share the sweet juicy fruit.

The servant shivered, hurried back to his canoe, and paddled away. As soon as he was out of sight, the sky darkened. The air filled with the swoosh of wings. Clouds and clouds of flying foxes swooped down, bringing the princess food and chirping their encouragement. Leutogi sang to them her thanks. And then she began a different song, a new chant. She sang about a new legend, the story of a Samoan princess who rescued an injured flying fox, offered food and friendship, and was repaid a **thousand-fold**.

thousandfold
a thousand times

HOW COUNTING CAME TO TOKELAU

Fakaofo
  fah kah OH foh

Sina   SEE nah

Ulu   OO loo

Iva   EE vah

Valu   VAH loo

Fitu   FEE too

Ono   OH noh

Lima   LEE mah

Fa   fah

Tolu   TOH loo

Lua   LOO ah

Tasi   TAH see

At one time in the distant past, all of our islands counted from ten to one. We did not count from one to ten as we do now. This story will tell how this has come to be.

On **Fakaofo** Atoll lived an old woman. Her name was **Sina**. She had ten sons and a single lovely daughter, also named Sina. Sina loved all of her children. She would call them when it was time to eat, or play, or do some work around the village. When she called her boys, she would say their names in the order of their age. "**Ulu**, **Iva**, **Valu**, **Fitu**, **Ono**, **Lima**, **Fa**, **Tolu**, **Lua**, **Tasi**," which is to say, "Ten, Nine, Eight, Seven, Six, Five, Four, Three, Two, One." "Come in, it is time for you to eat!" When they heard this, the ten hungry boys ran into the hut. At other times she would call, "It is time to go to bed." The boys came in a good deal more slowly. They were good boys, but they did NOT want to go to bed.

Tasi was the youngest. His name was always called last.

"Can't you call me first, Mama?" he asked.

"No, my son," Sina replied. "I must always call my sons in order. Your older brothers have the honor of being first, because they were the first."

"Well, someday I will be first, too!" Tasi declared.

One sad day Fakaofo was visited by a terrible **cannibal**, **Saipuniana**. He threatened to eat everyone unless he was given a wife. Sina-the-Daughter was given to Saipuniana as his wife. He took her to **Fiti**, which is now called Fiji, and kept her there as his prisoner.

For many years Sina-the-Mother **grieved** for her daughter, but what could she do? Then one day, her ten sons had become young men. They decided they would each build a canoe and rescue their sister! Their mother was so happy!

The ten brothers raced into the jungle to find trees for their canoes. Soon the eldest, Ulu, was far in front of the others. "I will finish my canoe first and rescue Sina. My mother will be so proud and I will be the chief!" So he hurried on, until he suddenly came upon a startling sight.

In front of him an old man was locked in a deadly struggle with a large serpent. "Help me!" cried the old man, whose name was **Sinota**. "I am nearly dead."

"I'm sorry, old man," said Ulu. "I am in a hurry. I cannot stop to help you or my brothers will get ahead of me. They will be here soon. You can get some help from them." Then Ulu hurried on into the forest. In truth, Ulu was afraid of the snake, but he did not tell Sinota this.

This same sad story happened over and over as Iva, Valu, Fitu, Ono, Lima, Fa, Tolu and Lua all found Sinota being crushed by the snake. "I am sorry, old man," they all told him. "We are in a great hurry and cannot stop to help you or the others will rescue our sister first." They all passed by, leaving Sinota alone with the monstrous snake.

Finally, little Tasi came along, much later than all the others. By the time he arrived, Sinota was

cannibal
someone who eats human flesh

Saipuniana
sye poo nee AH nah

Fiti   FEE tee

grieved
felt sorrow

Sinota
see NOH tah

machete
large, heavy
knife

nearly finished. "Help me," he gasped. Tasi was afraid too, but he took his **machete** and struck the monster snake right on the neck. He cut the head clean off that snake, and Sinota was free!

"I am very grateful," said Sinota. "Is there any way I can help you?"

"I don't think so," answered Tasi. "You are old and very weak. I need to build a canoe to go and rescue my sister!"

"Don't be so sure I cannot help," replied Sinota. He spoke some magic words and suddenly the whole clearing was full of little insects—spiders, ants, and all sorts of bugs.

Sinota seemed to know all of the insects by name. "Go find the best canoe tree," he told the flying insects.

When they returned with their news, Sinota spoke to the ants. "Go and cut down the tree. Chew it to make a canoe!" The ants were very tiny, but there were many thousands of them. They all marched off into the forest. Tasi and Sinota followed.

By the time Tasi got to the middle of the forest, the ants had already finished the canoe, and a group of spiders had almost finished weaving the sail. It was beautiful!

"But my brothers are already far ahead," cried Tasi.

"Don't worry," counseled Sinota. "When you see their canoes you must speak quietly this special word." Then Sinota whispered a magic word into Tasi's ear.

Tasi set off at once. His canoe was so light, and the sail so quick, that he soon overtook his first brother, Lua. Then Tasi whispered the word and the wind stopped blowing into Lua's sail. Lua's canoe stopped right where it was.

Tasi blew on by and soon overtook Tolu, and then Fa, Lima, Ono, Fitu, Valu, Iva, and Ulu. In each case the effect was the same. As soon as he whispered the magic word, the wind stopped blowing and Tasi sailed by. He reached Fiti long before any of the others.

There he found his sister sitting in front of her hut, crying.

"I have come to take you home to see our mother!" announced Tasi.

But Sina was frightened. "My husband is a cruel cannibal! He will kill you and eat you if you try to take me away." She began to cry again, but Tasi told her his plan.

"Tonight you must tell your husband you are too hot in the hut. Come to this tree and I will be waiting for you."

"But he watches me all the time."

"Then tell him to hold the end of this rope, which you will hold when you are gone."

That night, Sina told her cannibal-husband, Saipuniana, "I am very hot. I will go and cool off under the tree near the beach. Take this cord and tie it around my waist. If you keep the end here with you, you will know I have not run off!"

When Sina got to the beach, Tasi was waiting for her. He carefully untied the rope and retied it around a branch of the tree. Then he put Sina into his canoe and silently pushed out into the **lagoon**.

When Sina was gone from the hut for a long time, Saipuniana pulled the rope. He heard the noise of the tree branches rustling where the rope was tied. He thought it was Sina signaling him.

Still later, when Sina was STILL gone from the hut, Saipuniana got impatient. He pulled the rope really hard, intending to pull Sina back to the hut.

lagoon
    shallow body of water, often surrounded by a reef or an atoll

Instead the branch broke. When Saipuniana pulled the rope into the hut, he found a broken branch, but no sign of Sina!

Saipuniana was furious. He ran out of the hut. Out in the lagoon he could just make out the tiny canoe. Saipuniana knew magic. He called upon the mist over the water.

"Mist come. Make the water hard so I can run and catch my wife."

The mist came, and the water became as hard as a stone path. Saipuniana ran after the canoe. He was a very swift runner and soon overtook the fleeing canoe.

When Tasi saw that Saipuniana was gaining, he whispered yet another magic word that Sinota had taught him. The word brought the storm clouds. The driving rain soaked Saipuniana to the skin, but Sina and Tasi were warm and dry! Saipuniana was shivering with cold by the time he caught them. He barely had the strength to crawl into the canoe.

Tasi saw how cold Saipuniana was. He slyly offered to wrap Saipuniana in a large sleeping mat to keep him warm. Saipuniana gladly accepted this help, thinking, "I can warm up first, and eat them later!"

When Saipuniana was all wrapped up in the mat, Tasi took coconut fiber and sewed the mat tightly closed. Then he took a great anchor rock, tied it to the mat, and threw Saipuniana overboard. That was the end of the cannibal.

While Tasi was struggling with Saipuniana, the other brothers returned, empty-handed, to Fakaofo. Sina-the-Mother asked the returning brothers if they had rescued their sister. They all answered, sadly, "No, we did not. I am afraid that she is dead, and our youngest brother, Tasi, as well."

Sina-the-Mother was brokenhearted. She had lost so much. Then another canoe appeared on the horizon. It was Tasi, and in his canoe he brought much joy. He brought home his sister, Sina!

Now Sina-the-Mother was overjoyed. She ordered a great **feast** in the village.

feast
meal often accompanied by celebration or entertainment

"Tasi," she said. "I know now that you are not the last of my sons, but the first! From this day on, when I call my boys, I will call you first, and all of the others will come after."

Tasi, Lua, Tolu, Fa, Lima, Ono, Fitu, Valu, Iva, Ulu.

And that is how we count, from one to ten. And Tasi is always number one.

RORI-OF-THE-ROCKS

Rori   ROH ree

Mangaia
mahn GYE ah

hermit
  someone who
  lives apart from
  others

Una   OO nah

Rongo-ariki
rahn goh ah REE
kee

sennit
  strong cord

Amio
ah MEE oh

*On the island of **Mangaia** once lived a famous **hermit**, known as Rori-of-the-West or Rori-of-the-Rocks. This is his story.*

Rori's grandfather was **Una**, and his father was **Rongo-ariki**. Both Una and Rongo-ariki were great craftsmen. They knew how to carve beautiful canoes and tools from wood, and how to weave the strongest **sennit** from coconut fiber. They also had the secret knowledge of how to carve images of the gods. Una and Rongo-ariki kept this knowledge safe and passed it on to Rori when he was a young man.

Rori and his sister were very happy living on Mangaia. Rori was a fast runner and loved especially to climb the steep cliffs that surrounded his village.

In those days, there was much fighting. The day finally came when a battle was fought right in Rori's village!

It was a terrible battle. Both Rori's beloved father, Rongo-ariki, and his lovely sister, **Amio**, were killed. Just before he died, Rongo-ariki instructed his son, "Fly, Rori, fly to the black rocks and keep our family knowledge safe."

Rori obeyed his father, though it hurt him terribly to leave his side. He climbed up the steep cliffs, so fast that none of his enemies could get even close.

From far above the valley, he watched as his village was burned and his friends killed or captured.

Rori sadly turned from the valley and **surveyed** his new home. He was in a small valley, full of razor-sharp rocks. There were caves here in which he could hide, and the pointed stones would slow down any enemy spies.

surveyed
took a careful and complete look at

Night after night Rori built up his hiding place. He smoothed hundreds of tiny sharp pebbles until he made a smooth path on which he could run in case someone was chasing him. Rori put these small stones down so cleverly that even the slightest weight on the stones set off a low rumble, a sound that alerted Rori to danger.

All of his work was successful, for he remained undiscovered for many years. He was all but forgotten by the villagers. They thought he had died in the rocky waste.

Using the skills his father taught him, Rori was able to make sharp tools. Using his special path and strong body, Rori was able to slip quietly into the **fertile** valleys when it was dark. There he could find fresh food, especially fruits and the nuts of the mahogany tree. Rori was so clever that he always replaced the good nuts he found in the valley with rotten nuts he found in the rocks. This way, no one ever suspected someone was stealing from the village trees. To this day, mahogany nuts are called "Rori's Chestnuts" or "Rori's Delight."

fertile
producing much plant life

The seasons passed. Rori was no longer young. His skin was as dry and sunburned as an old leather hide. But he could still run over the rocks faster than any man alive. On one or two occasions, when Rori became careless in his food-gathering, men tried to capture him. But Rori was too fast. He would leap high into the air, landing on the rocks and disappearing like the mist.

Finally, Rori became lonely for the company of others. He had lived alone, like a hermit, for almost all of his life. One time before, he had tried to return to live among people. He thought all of his former enemies were dead. He was mistaken, and was lucky to escape back to the rocks before he was killed and eaten!

This time, his enemies were truly gone. For the first time in years, the whole island was at peace. But there was no one left with the skills to carve images of their gods. No one but the scarcely remembered Rori-of-the-Rocks.

From time to time a shriveled and burnt old man had been sighted, but he had always been too quick to be captured. "This old man must be Rori," thought **Manaune**, who had known Rori when he was still a young man. "This man will have the knowledge we need to make our carvings."

Manuane
mah noo AH neh

Manaune called to the rocks where Rori was known to hide, far above the villagers below. "Rori, come back! Come back and teach me to carve my god!"

Rori heard the calling and was shocked. He had not heard anyone speak his name for many years. Was this some sort of trick?

When Rori realized that it was Manaune, whom he trusted, and that peace had come to their island, he agreed to return to the village on Mangaia. Great was the joy at his return.

Rori lived with his people for many more years, until the coming of Captain Cook. He carved images of the many gods of his people. He instructed the young people in the arts of carving and weaving. He even had time to get married and have sons of his own!

To this day, the people of these islands have the special skills and knowledge brought back to them by Rori, the hermit of the rocks.

HINA AND HER LOVER EEL

Hina-Moe-Aitu
hee nah moy aye too

Mangaia
mahn GYE ah

Hina-Moe-Aitu is the name of a girl who lived on **Mangaia**. The island was encircled by an ancient reef. Tall, steep cliffs faced both the land and the sea. Hina knew of a private pool below a tall cliff. She had it all to herself. Every day she went there alone to bathe in its warm, sweet-smelling water. The pool was the home of many eels, some of them **massive** in size. They loved the dark, quiet bottom of Hina's pool.

massive very big

One day when Hina had slipped into the **caressing** water of her pool, a giant eel rose up beneath her. It rubbed itself back and forth against her nakedness. She allowed the eel to rub her. It felt good, and no one was watching. Many days passed as Hina continued to bathe and let the eel visit her.

caressing
touching lovingly

Early one morning, as the sun was still rising behind the cliff, the eel changed into a handsome young man. He said to her, "I am **Tuna**, the god of the eels. You are so lovely that I have left my watery home to come stay with you."

Tuna too nah

And so they left the pool where they had met. Together they went to Hina's house and conducted themselves as lovers do. They were devoted to each other. Always, Tuna became an eel once again after visiting Hina. In this way they kept their love a secret.

One day in the season of breadfruit, Tuna told Hina that he must leave her. Already the tears began to flow from her eyes.

"Shhhh," said Tuna softly. "Keep your tears, for there will be water everywhere soon. Tomorrow the heavens will split open and the rains will come. The sky will pour rivers onto the land. The waters of the rivers will overflow and become oceans. Everything will become like the pool where we met, but it will not be glassy and calm."

Hina stared at Tuna with round, frightened eyes. "The water will flood the taro patches. It will lick the floor of your parents' house. It will rise and rise, washing away the mats and sucking things toward the sea. But you, my dear, have no need to be frightened. I will swim to you, for I am a creature of the water. Do not run away! You must wait for me to come. I will lay my head in the doorway. You must grab the **adze** of your great-grandfather and cut off my head. Then you must push against the rising water until you reach the high ground. Bury my head there. Visit that place every day and see what is there. Do not fail me in this, Hina."

Hina did as Tuna told her she must. Rain began to fall that night, thick as *tapa* before it is pounded, heavy as fresh green branches. Down, down it fell until she thought it was filling up her throat. By morning, the land was covered with the sea. Water slap-slapped against the walls of her parents' house.

A great eel came to the house. As it crossed the **threshold**, she took the adze and cut off its head. Then she waded up to the highest cliff and buried the eel's great head. Once the head had been planted, the rain **ceased**. The floods slid slowly back into the sea.

Each day Hina visited the place where her lover's

adze
  cutting tool with a thin arched blade

tapa
  cloth made from pounded mulberry bark

threshold
  doorway

ceased stopped

183

head lay buried. For a long while, she waited. Finally, a strong green shoot thrust up through the soil. Hina knew that such a shoot had never been seen on Mangaia before. She watched over it carefully. The very next day it was joined by another.

Hina watched over the green shoots. Slowly, they grew into two strong trees as straight and beautiful as the backs of young men. They grew taller and taller until their rustling **fronds** brushed against the sky. By then, Hina had children. They grew taller and taller too, until they were able to climb the trees and gather their round, heavy fruit.

These were the first coconuts. One was reddish, the **sacred** nut of **Tangaroa**. It gave *niu*, which was sweet and delicious to drink. The other was green, the sacred fruit of **Rongo**. This one contained *niu mata*, creamy white flesh. From these trees and their branches and fruits, the people made their houses, thatched their roofs, filled their stomachs, and pressed fragrant oils that made their skin **glisten**. They ate from bowls made of coconut shells. They even used the tree to make sturdy paddles for their outrigger canoes.

These were the gifts of the Eel God to his lover Hina. And this is why the delicate flesh of the coconut is called *te roro o te Tuna*, "the brains of Tuna." Look for yourself! Take the husk from the coconut and look at the bare, ripe nut. Do you see the face of Tuna, with his sad lover's eyes and his eager mouth, longing for Hina?

fronds leaves

sacred
worthy of respect

Tangaroa
tahn gah ROH ah

niu   NEE oo

Rongo
RAHN goh

niu mata
nee oo mah tah

glisten shine

te roro o te Tuna
teh roh roh oh teh too nah

TONGA

THE CREATION OF THE TONGAN ISLANDS, PEOPLE, AND KINGS

Tangaloa, the god of art and invention, sat in his sky home of **Bolotu**, where death was not known and decay did not exist. He looked down at the **vast** south sea. "I am hungry. Hungry for fish." He got out his great turtle hook and let it go down, down, down to the sea far below. Soon something big and heavy pulled on the line.

Tangaloa pulled and pulled, but he could not pull up the hook. He **peered** down at the ocean and laughed. He had not caught a fish. He had caught an enormous rock! No, a whole row of rocks. He yanked and tugged. He could not shake loose his hook. He laughed again and rubbed his empty stomach. "Today I will not eat," he said. "Today I shall have great fun making islands."

Tangaloa pulled up the very bottom of the sea. Just as the rocky tip was about to break through the surface, the fishing line broke. Instead of remaining one long continent, the land broke into dozens of islands.

*If you wonder if this story is true, go to **Tongatapu** and there you will see a rock with a hole about two feet in diameter. This is the hole that held the great fishing hook of Tangaloa. If your doubts still are not satisfied, go speak with **Tu'i Tonga**, the **divine***

Tangaloa
tahn gah LOH ah
Bolotu
boh LOH too
vast　very large

peered　looked

Tongatapu
tawng ah TAH poo
Tu'i Tonga
too ee TAWNG ah
divine
　related to the gods

185

chief. Until only a few years ago, he still possessed this mighty hook. Unfortunately, when his house caught on fire and burned right to the ground, the sacred basket that held the hook was burned to ashes. Those who know this fishing story know also that the hook was made of tortoise shell from Samoa and strengthened with a whale bone.

Matua
mah TOO ah

Tufunga
too FOONG ah

Etumatatupua
eh too mah tah
too POO ah

After fishing up islands, the great Tangaloa **Matua** decided to create something to live on the beautiful islands. He called his two sons, Tangaloa **Tufunga** and Tangaloa **Etumatatupua**. The sons sat next to their father, who was sitting cross-legged, carving. They waited a long time. Until their father spoke, they would remain silent.

Tangaloa set down the wood he was carving. He pointed the long knife at the pile of shavings. "Look, my sons. I will shake down these wooden shavings. Let them mix with the water. Good. Now," he said to one of his sons, "become a little brown **plover** and fly down and tell me what you see."

plover
  shorebird with a
  short bill

His son became a plover and flew down to earth. Unfortunately, all he saw was wooden shavings floating on the sea. This he reported to his father.

Day after day Tangaloa Matua continued carving and shaking the shavings down to earth. Each day his son flew down as a plover. But each day he reported that nothing had changed.

Finally, one day when he flew down to earth, Matua's son was amazed to see that the shavings had become a lovely little island. He flew back to his father. "What a beautiful island you have created!"

Tangaloa Matua smiled. "Good. Now put this seed in your beak. Plant it on that island."

Soon the seed grew a creeper vine. The vine grew and grew until it covered the island. The plover flew down. He pecked at the root until it split in two. Then the root quickly rotted. All this the plover reported back to his father.

Again Tangaloa Matua smiled. "Now you will be surprised. Fly back one more time. Look carefully in the warm damp place where the root is rotting."

The plover returned to the island and found a big juicy white worm. He pecked it. The worm split in two. From the top, a man came out. This man the gods called **Kohai**. The lower part of the worm also turned into a man. This man was called **Kuau**. The little plover felt something stuck to his beak. He shook his head. A tiny piece of the worm fell off. This third piece turned into a man called **Momo**.

Very pleased with what had been created, the gods then named the island **Eueiki**, the first island inhabited by men. These first men of Tonga began the long line of the earliest rulers, the Tu'i Tongas. Kohai was the first man. But he came from a worm. **Ahoei** would be the first true man, for he would be born from a woman, a beautiful woman who mated with the great god Tangaloa. His birth, the birth of Ahoei, would continue the divine line of Tongan kings. It would also cause many troubles!

Ahoei is still considered the first ruler of Tonga. Both Tongans and Western historians have **calculated** that Ahoei lived in A.D. 950. He began the divine line of Tu'i Tongas, the royal kings of Tonga. The members of this royal family ruled one after the other until the death of King **Laufilitoga**. This forty-eighth and final Tu'i Tonga died in 1865.

This first true man and first Tu'i Tonga, Ahoei, was half human and half divine. Ahoei's mother was the beautiful earth maiden **Ilaheva Ve'epopua**. Little is known about how she came to be.

Ahoei's father was the god Tangaloa. This

Kohai
koh HAH ee

Kuau
koo AH oo

Momo   moh moh

Eueiki
eh oo eh EE kee

Ahoei
ah hoh EH ee

calculated
figured out
mathematically

Laufilitoga
lah oo fee lee TOH
gah

Ilaheva Ve'epopua
ee lah HEH vah
veh eh poh POO
ah

brazen young god, Tangaloa, came down to earth from heaven by climbing down a huge ironwood tree. The ironwood tree liked to tease Tangaloa. The tree was so tall its branches scraped the clouds. Sometimes it caused the rain to fall. It dared the lizards and geckoes to scamper up. It dared Tangaloa to climb down to the world.

There on earth Tangaloa saw an irresistible scene. The beautiful maiden, Ilaheva, was wading in the tide pools searching for shellfish. Her long black hair flowed down her smooth golden back like seaweed flowing in a gentle ocean current. Her dark flashing eyes sparkled with delight as she discovered bright blue starfish hiding under coral rocks. Tangaloa stared at her. He felt as if his heart were suddenly being tossed and tumbled in the waves of the sea.

When he was in heaven, all Tangaloa could think about was returning to earth. That is exactly what he did. There the beautiful woman, Ilaheva, waited where the waves kissed the shore. Tangaloa visited her often. But he had his own wife and children in the sky. He was lonely for his sky family. His trips down the ironwood to see Ilaheva became fewer and fewer until there were none at all.

But Ilaheva found that she would soon have a child. A beautiful boy was born to her. She named him Ahoei, "day of exclamation." The boy grew to handsome manhood. Eventually he asked to visit his father.

Ilaheva knew the journey to the heavens would be dangerous. It was important for Ahoei to know his father. The wise mother oiled her son's body with sweet-smelling sandalwood oil. She then draped a **tapa** cloth over his shoulders. He was ready for his dangerous journey. She showed Ahoei the ironwood tree once so often used by his father.

Many other instructions Ilaheva gave to her son to protect him. All of these instructions Ahoei followed. Sadly, when Ahoei's divine step-brothers saw him they immediately hated him. They were afraid this earth brother would be favored by their father. Enraged with jealousy and fear, they killed Ahoei. With one swift slice, they cut off his head, threw it into the bushes, and ate his body.

Ahoei's father, the great god Tangaloa, learned of this brutal slaying. He ordered his sons to find Ahoei's head. He set it in a sacred **kava** bowl. Then he commanded his sons to vomit into the bowl. All night the step-brothers were ordered to stand around the kava bowl.

kava
    drink that is like a drug

At dawn a strange light filled the skies. Something began moving in the bowl. Ahoei rose up from the bowl, whole and healed.

Tangaloa commanded his sons: "Ahoei came here in peace and friendship. You treated him with hate and jealousy. Go down to earth. All of you! Ahoei shall be the earthly king ruling over all of you. He shall be known as Tu'i Tonga, the King of Tonga. He and his children shall rule Tonga forever."

THE TALE OF THE *BOUNTY*

This story of Pitcairn Island begins in 1787, just a few years after the American Revolution. Another **revolution** was about to take place.

Lt. William **Bligh** was a good-looking seaman in the British Navy. He had sailed with the famous Captain Cook. Lieutenant Bligh always dreamed of having his own ship to command.

The British at that time had many **plantations** in the British West Indies. They used slave labor to do most of the work. Captain Cook had discovered breadfruit in Tahiti. This healthful food grew on trees. The British hoped they could use breadfruit to feed their slaves. A small ship, the *Bounty,* was sent with a load of breadfruit seedlings from Tahiti to the plantations. Lieutenant Bligh got his wish. He was named captain of the *Bounty.*

Bligh was a strict captain. When he was angry he often insulted his officers and his crew. One time, when the men refused to eat spoiled pumpkin, he exploded, "You dam'd **infernal scoundrels**. I'll make you eat grass. . . ."

The voyage was hard and long. First Bligh tried to sail the short way around the tip of South America. The weather was awful. Storms kept battering the poor ship until all the food was wet or spoiled. Bligh finally gave up trying to "make the Horn."

revolution
the overthrow of one ruler by another

Bligh bly

plantations
large farms with many workers

infernal
relating to hell

scoundrels
rascals

190

This time Bligh sailed to Tahiti the long way—around the tip of Africa, below Australia. The *Bounty* finally reached Tahiti ten months after leaving England.

Tahiti must have seemed a paradise to the crew. It had fresh food and water. It had beautiful women. It even gave the crew the chance to escape Bligh's **blistering** insults. Bligh, on the other hand, went about his business gathering breadfruit.

blistering
severe

After four months, the *Bounty* was ready to set sail for the Indies. The ship was crowded with breadfruit seedlings. Bligh's insults and temper had not improved. The *Bounty* set sail for Tonga.

Fletcher Christian was the mate on the *Bounty*. He was only twenty-two years old when they sailed. By the time the *Bounty* reached Tonga, one thousand miles west of Tahiti, he was ready to jump ship and escape on a wooden raft. He could not stand any more of Bligh's insults. Some of the men heard of his plan and asked him to wait. "There are others who want to join you. Perhaps there is another way." By the next day, an unplanned **mutiny** had begun.

mutiny revolt

Twenty-five men stayed with Christian. Eighteen stayed with Bligh. Bligh and his men were given food and water, but no weapons and no maps. They were set adrift in a small twenty-three–foot boat in the open ocean. The *Bounty* and Christian sailed away, tossing the breadfruit overboard, pot by pot.

First Christian tried to settle on the island of **Tubuai**, about three hundred miles from Tahiti. Soon the rough mutineers got into a fight with the local natives. Several men were killed. The *Bounty* beat a **hasty** retreat to Tahiti. The bay in Tubuai is still called "Bloody Bay."

Tubuai
toob WAH ee

hasty very fast

When the *Bounty* returned to Tahiti, without Bligh and without the breadfruit, Christian made up a story, saying, "We met Captain Cook at sea. He took the breadfruit and some of the crew on his ship. They are on their way to the Indies. We have been ordered to take a load of supplies for a settlement in Australia." Christian knew that the true story would soon be out. He would be a wanted man. He was eager to get away from Tahiti as soon as possible.

The *Bounty* returned to Tubuai. Christian tried to build a safe fort there. Many of the men were not happy when Christian announced plans to burn the *Bounty* to hide her from the British Navy. They wanted to return to Tahiti and take their chances there. Christian knew this was dangerous. Most of the men decided to go to Tahiti. Only nine mutineers, including Fletcher Christian, were left on the *Bounty.*

uninhabited
having no people living there

This time, Christian and the mutineers sailed west, back toward Tonga. They were looking for an **uninhabited** island. They didn't find a single one.

Just a few months after the *Bounty* left Tahiti, a large Navy ship, the *Pandora,* docked. It was under orders to search the Pacific for the mutineers. All the men remaining on Tahiti were unlucky. They were quickly rounded up and **put in irons**. The *Pandora* set sail for England, where they would stand trial. The mutineers' bad luck continued. The *Pandora* struck a rock on the Great Barrier Reef. Four of the mutineers drowned. Only ten mutineers made it back to England to stand trial. Seven were set free, but three were hanged for their part in the mutiny.

put in irons
chained up by the hands and feet

Fletcher Christian now knew there were no

safe islands to the west. He had once read of an uninhabited island far to the east of Tahiti, back the way they had come. He decided to look for this place, called "Pitcairn."

It took another two months before the *Bounty* found Pitcairn Island. The men saw an isolated volcanic peak, only one mile wide and two miles long. There were no beaches and no people. It was perfect!

They pulled their boat into a small indentation in the rocky cliffs, a place since known as "Bounty Bay." Then, with many different emotions, they burned the *Bounty* and watched her sink into the ocean.

Before the *Bounty* left Tahiti, Christian had taken aboard several Tahitian men and women. Some of these were kidnapped by inviting them to a party and giving them too much to drink. After they were asleep, the boat set sail. By the time they awoke, the *Bounty* was already far out to sea. The original plan was to have one woman for every man. Three Tahitian men **stowed away** on the boat, making three more men than women. This was a great mistake, and only one man would live to enjoy this island.

stowed away
hid in order to go on the voyage

Pitcairn could have been perfect. It had lush vegetation and good fresh water. The original Polynesian inhabitants were long gone. They left behind large stone carvings and statues like those found a thousand miles away on Easter Island. Pitcairn had everything, and it was theirs! Christian and his woman soon had a son who was born on a Thursday in October. They named him "Thursday October Christian." Other sons and daughters followed.

Then one of the mutineer's women died from an

infection. Another woman died in a fall from the cliffs. Both mutineers demanded a woman from the Tahitian men. This caused much anger.

The mutineers were violent men. They killed two of the Tahitian men. Two years later, the remaining Tahitian men got revenge. They murdered five of the mutineers, including Christian. More and more fighting followed. Eventually all the Tahitian men were killed.

Of the four remaining mutineers, one was murdered by the others. Another got drunk and fell to his death from the cliffs. A third died less than a year later during an asthma attack. Only one mutineer, ten Tahitian women, and all the children remained.

In 1808, an American ship, the *Topaz*, stopped at Pitcairn. This was the first vessel to land since the arrival of the mutineers. The crew was greeted by a handsome young man. "My name is Thursday October Christian," he said. When the Americans left, they told this remarkable story to the British.

The British had little time to go searching for mutineers on a far-distant island. But in 1814 two ships from the British Navy finally arrived at Pitcairn. They found the one living mutineer, calling himself "John Adams." Twenty-five years after the mutiny, the British decided to let this man live his final years in peace.

The story of Pitcairn is not really the story of Bligh. His is a remarkable tale as well. Somehow the tiny boat survived. Bligh managed to sail over 3,500 miles to reach the coast of Australia, barely finding a passage through the **treacherous** Great Barrier Reef. This passage is still known as "Bligh's Channel." From Australia he and his crew returned to England. Less than a year later Bligh was again in command of a ship. This time he completed his original mission. He took a shipment of breadfruit from Tahiti to the British West Indies. Without a mutiny.

treacherous
full of hidden
dangers

TANGAROA CREATES THE GREAT SHELL OF THE WORLD

Tangaroa
tahn gah ROH ah

dwelled lived

realm   kingdom

infinite
  going on forever

In Tahiti, Tangaroa is the ancestor of all gods. He **dwelled** in the **realm** of darkness, for there was no light. There was nothing at all, just Tangaroa and the shell in which he lived. For an **infinite** stretch of time, Tangaroa lived in blackness. There was no moon pulling the tides. There was no water and no land. No trees or crabs or waving wands of soft coral. There was no salty taste in your mouth after swimming because there was no water, no salt, and no you. There were no people or fish, rats or roosters. There were no sand-fleas or coconuts or black-tipped sharks. There was nothing.

This is how it was until Tangaroa turned over inside his shell, causing the great shell to crack. He turned again. The great shell fell open. He stepped out of the darkness and called out: "Who is there up above me?" Silence was his only answer.

"Who is there below me?"

Again, there was no answer.

"Who is there in front of me? Who is there behind me?"

Still, there was only silence. Tangaroa felt something growing deep within him, a feeling of great anger.

"Rocks!" he cried out. "Come to me!"

But there were no rocks, so nothing came.

"Sand!" he yelled. "Crawl to my feet and lay yourself down!"

There was no sand.

"Wind," roared Tangaroa. "Blow sand to me."

But there was no wind. Only a great, empty silence.

Tangaroa, the divine one, was angry at this disobedience. He lifted up the enormous shell in which he had dwelled for so very long. Slowly, very slowly, he turned the heavy shell over. The round, unbroken half became a dome and was now the sky. Tangaroa named it **Rumia**, the Overturned.

Rumia
roo MEE ah

After that, Tangaroa rested. But he grew restless and tired of being alone. He took another huge shell and smashed it into pieces. It formed millions of rocks and tiny grains of sand.

Still, silence filled the world. Tahaki was boiling with anger at how nothing obeyed him. The great Tangaroa needed something to command. So he reached inside his own body and drew forth his backbone. He threw it onto the shell fragments that had turned to rock and sand. It became a majestic mountain range. His ribs were still attached to the backbone. They became the ridges, cliffs, and hills that towered over the sand.

Tangaroa reached back inside himself and pulled out his inner organs. He flung them into the sky-dome. They became the white clouds that float overhead. Sometimes they fill with water, as they did inside Tangaroa, and rain down upon the land.

Then he used his raw, red flesh to bring richness and fertility to the earth, that plants and animals could grow upon it. His legs and arms made the world solid, so it would hold together and not slide off into the sea. One by one he plucked out his fingernails and toenails. These he offered to the fishes and shell-creatures for scaly skin and houses for the crabs.

This god wore feathers like a bird. He plucked his feathers to make the breadfruit and the **pandanus**. He made all the plants whose tops are green and whose roots drink water from the land. Then he pulled out his long intestines, long, wet armfuls! From these he made eels and shrimps and spiny lobsters, which live in fresh streams and the salty ocean.

Tangaroa worked so hard to make the world that his blood ran hot. His body had become an open cave after all these gifts he had offered, so his blood spilled out and floated away. Some went up into the sky and made the sunsets and sunrises glow red. Some hid in the clouds to become rainbows after a storm. All that is now red was made from Tangaroa's blood that floated away that day.

Tangaroa's head remained on his body. And because he was a god, because he was **sacred**, his body also remained. He had made the world and yet he lived on. From that time forth, everything became ripe and fertile. The world grew and grew.

Next, Tangaroa called upon the other gods to come dwell in the heavens and the earth with him. Finally, when the world was ready and the gods had come, he made human beings.

In the beginning of the world, there was a shell. From this shell, the sky was made. A shell is endless, curved space. Inside, the gods put our sun, our moon, the planets that burn red in the night sky, and all the shining stars in all the heavens.

Think of it: the land is a shell that holds up the streams running over it. It is a shell for the animals that walk across it and the plants whose roots dig into it. The shell of a man is woman, since man is

pandanus
plant fiber used for weaving mats, baskets, and other products

sacred
worthy of respect

198

born of woman. The shell of a woman is woman, for only within her flesh can another woman take form. Inside a shell, there is life. Waiting in darkness, turning and turning, preparing to be born.

TAHAKI, THE GOLDEN-SKINNED BOY

Tahaki
tah HAH kee

ancestor
family member who came before, like a great-great grandparent

Rona Nihoniho Roroa
ROH nah nee hoh nee hoh roh ROH ah

Hina   hee nah

Taharaa
tah hah RAH ah

Monoi   moh noy

crevice
narrow opening

Tahaki of the Golden Skin is an **ancestor** of the people of Tahiti. Tahaki's grandmother was **Rona Nihoniho Roroa**, which means Rona of the Long Teeth. Though she was beautiful, Rona did terrifying things with her teeth. Her constant hunger for human flesh made it hard for her to keep a husband.

Rona gave birth to a daughter she named **Hina**. At first Rona was a good mother. She hid her human-flesh–eating habits from everyone. Rona rubbed Hina's body with sweet sandalwood oil. When Hina was just a baby, Rona gently pressed her head into a pretty, round shape. She even smoothed Hina's tiny fingers over and over so they would grow long and slender.

When Hina was sleeping, Rona caught people who passed along the beach path near **Taharaa**. She dragged them into a cave and ate them, leaving only their bones.

After many years, when Hina had become a young woman, a handsome boy named **Monoi** fell in love with her and she with him. They met every day in a secret place, a rocky, shady **crevice** that would open and close when they said magic words.

Rona became suspicious of her daughter's absences. One day she followed Hina through the forest and discovered her with Monoi. When she saw his handsome body, she hungered for human flesh. How delicious his young brown muscles! How tender the marrow hidden inside his bones!

The next day Rona made Hina cut palm leaves and sweep the earth around their house. She ordered her to keep cutting and sweeping until it was all done. Rona stole away to the secret rock and disguised her voice as Hina's. But Monoi could tell it wasn't his beloved Hina. Alas, Rona had overheard the words for splitting open the rock: **Te tumu o te papa e, vahia**! Rona rushed in. She grabbed Monoi and gobbled him up! Her favorite parts were ears and toes and brains. When she pried apart Monoi's ribs to eat his heart, it was missing.

That night, Hina came to meet Monoi in their secret place. Instead of finding a lover ready to embrace her, she found his bloody bones. She also found his heart, still beating, waiting for her. Monoi's heart told her how to go to Chief **No'a Huruhuru**'s house. With Chief No'a she would be safe. First she must go home and fool Rona. Hina took a long banana branch and covered it with her *tapa* sleeping cloth. Where she usually lay her head, she put a drinking coconut. Then she ran!

Rona had gone crazy. She tried to take a huge bite out of the quietly sleeping body of her beloved daughter. When she saw she had been tricked with a branch and a coconut, she howled with rage. The frightened villagers told her where Hina had gone. By the time she got to No'a's house, Rona had grown hundreds of sharp teeth. Sharp yellow fangs were everywhere, on her arms and belly, hanging from her chin and spiking out of her knees!

No'a raised his spear against Rona. Down, down her long, sharp throat and into her belly it went. "Aaaargh!" she screamed, her hundreds of teeth

Te tumu o te papa e, vahia
teh too moo oh
teh pah pah eh,
vah hee ah

No'a Huruhuru
noh ah hoo roo
hoo roo

tapa
cloth made from
pounded
mulberry bark

201

rattling in agony as she died.

Hina stayed with Chief Noʻa. Together they had two sons. The older son was disobedient. When Hina asked him to check her head for lice, he refused. Her younger son, **Hema**, did as she asked. Hina told him, "Unlike your brother, you will have a fine wife."

Hema heh mah

When Hema grew up and was ready for a wife, his mother came to him. "Dig a hole in the bank of the **Vaipoʻopoʻo** river in the cool of morning," she said. "Hide in there and wait. A beautiful girl from the spirit world below will come to bathe. Grab her long, black hair with both hands. Don't let go! Carry her past four houses. If you make it that far, she will agree to come the rest of the way with you."

Vaipoʻopoʻo
vye poh oh poh oh

The next morning Hema grabbed the beautiful girl by the hair. But after he had carried her two houses, she pleaded, "Let me walk the rest of the way." Her voice was as soft and sweet as a mourning dove's. How could he say no? He put her down and she ran away.

"Do it again," Hina ordered him that night. "This time, do it right."

rushes
  reed-like plants
  with hollow
  stems

Hema hid in the **rushes** in the dew-filled morning. He grabbed the girl, wrapping her long hair around his hands. She struggled like a wild bird. Hema could feel her heart beating wildly under his hands. Still, he did not let go. He carried her past four houses and suddenly she went limp in his arms. After that, she was willing to stay with him. In time, a son, named Tahaki, was born, with the sunset's golden glow on his skin. He was **ehu**, golden-haired.

ehu eh hoo

Tahaki had a cousin, the son of his father Hema's disobedient brother. The two boys were good friends. But other boys were jealous of Tahaki. He was beautiful and golden, and he won almost all of the games. One day, the other boys beat Tahaki almost to death.

Tahaki's mother used her magic to bring Tahaki back to life. His father, Hema, upset that young people could be so cruel, went down to the dark underworld of **Po**, where cruel gods and dead people go. He didn't know that the gods of hell would kidnap him! They forced Hema to live in their toilet area, where they went to squat.

In the world above, Tahaki's mother watched over her son. She had Tahaki open his mouth above her head and breathe in her *iho*, her spirit of strength. Everyone could tell that he was of **divine** origin. He was the source of all that is golden-red: rocks, feathers, snapping fishes, blood-red flowers and golden-barked trees.

Tahaki of the Golden Skin grew to manhood. He cut the great fish called Tahiti with a magical **adze**. Tahiti changed from fish to earth. Tahaki chopped the islands just right so the land would grow fruit and root crops. With delicate strokes, he shaped the clouds and the rain. How else would there be shade to rest in and water to drink? He sculpted the mountains so the wind would sing as it passed. Because of him, Tahiti and many other islands rose up out of the eastern sea.

Tahaki was proud of his work. But he could not feel peace as long as his father was a prisoner. "How do I get to the dark world below?" he asked his mother. "I am old enough to go now."

"I will make the earth split open for you," she replied. "You may go with your cousin, but you must stay together in the pitch black. You will not even be able to see your own hand. Climb down, down, down, through the long line of caves. If you are brave enough, you will come to the Po."

Po   poh

iho   ee ho
divine
   related to the
   gods

adze
   cutting tool with
   a thin arched
   blade

Kuhi   koo hee

Tahaki and his cousin crept through dark, slimy caves. They slid their hands along muddy walls, but still they tripped and fell. Bruised and hungry, at last they came to a clearing full of light. They hid and watched an old, blind woman named **Kuhi** count a pile of yams over and over. "One, two, three, four, five," she chanted. Tahaki's cousin was so hungry he grabbed one of the yams. The blind woman cried, "What worm dares steal my food?"

Tahaki was afraid Kuhi would hurt his cousin, so he said, "It is Tahaki who has come."

"Aha! A boy from the lands above," she said. "You are of divine blood. You are welcome." She took a magical golden fishhook from her pocket and tied it to a fishing line. Tahaki knew not to touch it. But his cousin couldn't resist the spun gold dancing in the light. Once again his hand reached for what it should not touch.

gaping
  wide open

Kuhi hooked him like a giant fish! He tried to run away from her **gaping** mouth and fat belly. As he ran, she reeled him in.

"Let him go!" cried Tahaki.

"Never! He is my dinner," screamed Kuhi.

Tahaki grabbed his cousin and tore the hook from his flesh. Kuhi said, "So! There is a person of power here besides me. Boy, restore my sight!"

Tahaki said, "I will restore it." He threw two pieces of shiny white coconut into her eyes.

kinsmen relatives

Kuhi could see! Through her new eyes she saw that Tahaki and his cousin were her **kinsmen**. "Thank you!" she cried. "What can I do for you?" she asked.

"Tell us where to find my father, Hema," Tahaki said.

"Follow this road to the forest. Go to where the gods squat among the bushes. They have ripped out your father's eyes and made them into lights for girls who work all night weaving mats. The eye sockets are filled with bird droppings."

Tahaki was so horrified he could not speak. He ran to the place of the gods' filth. Hema lay as if dead in a wide pit filled with garbage and **excrement**. Tahaki gathered his father gently into his arms. "My poor father," he said. "I am so sorry."

excrement
   waste from the body

Hema raised his blind face and smiled weakly. "Tahaki, my golden boy," he murmured. "I thank you and the spirits who guided you." Father and son began to weep. Suddenly Tahaki remembered. "We must flee, father, before the evil gods find us! We are in terrible danger!"

When they were safely back in the land of sunlight, Tahaki carefully washed his father from the crown of his head to the crusty soles of his feet. Gently he placed his father's eyes back where they belonged. Golden-skinned Tahaki was happy to have both parents with him again.

THE LEGEND OF RATA

Tahaki
tah HAH kee

Rata rah tah

Puna poo nah

*Rata was the grandson of **Tahaki** of the Golden Skin. Soon after his birth, his parents were snatched by a giant demon-bird. The demon-bird gave Rata's mother to evil **Puna**. The demon-bird bit off Rata's father's head and swallowed it whole. Then he threw the headless body into the sea. Rata was raised by his grandmother. She did not tell him of his parents' terrible fate, but he found out from his playmates. He decided to go to Puna's land, the Horizon-of-the-Moon, to search for his parents.*

Rata did not go to search for his parents. Not yet. The years passed and he grew tall and full-chested, with strong muscles. The day came on which he would assume his mother's **sacred** clan title. He decided to have a boar chase to test the strength and bravery of the young men. His grandmother was to judge the contest, for all agreed she was wise. "Rata," she said to her grandson. "You are ***ariki nui*** now, the chief of all the clans. You must not take part in this chase. Join me as a judge instead."

Rata sat down with a great wreath of feathers on his head. The giant boar tore past. Men lunged at it with sharpened sticks. The wild pig shrieked with pain and anger. A great yell filled the clearing: "Kill the boar!"

sacred
  worthy of
  respect

ariki nui
ah ree kee noo ee

The boar came to a halt, bleeding and trembling. Suddenly, it rushed toward the thick forest of trees. A brave man dove for the boar's hind leg. The boar was crazed with the power of the gods. It escaped!

Rata stood up. His grandmother tugged on Rata's feather cloak. "No, no, Rata!" she said. "Sit down! You are a chief now." Rata sat down. The muddy boar slipped away and ran back to the ocean. Bloody foam spilled from its mouth. A man leaped upon its back, just missing its sharp tusks. The boar threw him off and ran to the sea.

Rata could stand it no longer. He tore off his headdress and his cloak. Then he dashed down to the water. Rata tried to grab the mud-slick boar. His fists tore wildly through the air. Rata was wilder than the boar itself! Rata smashed through the crowd of people, his clenched fists smashing like rocks. Bones crunched and skins were sliced open.

A great quiet came. The villagers were horrified. Everything stopped. The boar escaped into the mountains, but no one cared. The people were shocked to see their kinsmen dead at their feet. Rata hung his head in shame.

After that, Rata stayed inside his house. "You are unworthy of leading our people," his grandmother said harshly. "You are worse than the wild boar, for you have killed those who share your blood."

"O my grandmother," he cried. "I am terribly ashamed. Your words bruise my heart. It is worse than being beaten by your hands."

Then he said, "I know what I must do. I must overcome my shame and journey to the Horizon-of-the-Moon. I will avenge my father's death."

"First you must build a great canoe," answered his grandmother. "But you have no one to help you."

Rata took the sacred **adze** from his grandmother.

adze
cutting tool with a thin arched blade

He climbed up the steep hill to where mountains hide in a sea of clouds. He chopped down the tallest, straightest tree. All day he chopped. Just before sunset, the tree fell. Rata rested. When he awoke at sunrise, the tree was standing up again, its branches back on its sides! Again Rata chopped it down. This time he did not cut off its branches. He hid himself in the thickest part and waited.

Tiny forest people came. They leaped up into the branches and chanted, "Fly here, fly here, green leaves of our tree! Fly here, fly here, stand up, friend tree!"

Nothing happened. They tried a different chant. The tree rose up with all the tiny forest people still clinging to its branches.

Rata roared his anger: "B-a-a-a-a-a-a!" The tree shook mightily. The little forest people were flung into the air. Like dragonflies they hovered near the tree.

Now Rata used a gentle voice. "Please, I need this tree for my canoe," he asked the tree spirit, "to avenge my father's kidnapping."

Immediately the wind began to blow. The tree's leaves began to shake. A deep rumbling voice said, "Rata, the tree is yours." The forest people bowed to Rata, for surely he was a king. Then they flew away to the cave where they lived.

In the morning, Rata awoke to find two strong **hulls** with beautiful carvings on **bow** and **stern**. A densely woven sail was folded and ready. He was very proud, so proud he forgot to give thanks to the gods. His canoe leaked as soon as it slipped into the water.

His grandmother stood nearby, watching. How she laughed! "You look like a chief, Rata," she said, "but you are still partly a boy. Slow down. Remember

hull
 frame and outer covering of a boat

bow
 front part of a boat

stern
 rear part of a boat

your **ancestors'** spirits, remember the gods. You have much to learn." She showed him how to use breadfruit sap to plug the leaks. She smiled at him— sadly—and then she gave him a **pandanus** basket lined with soft *tapa* cloth. "This is for your father's head," she said softly.

Rata sailed with his loyal men toward the horizon. His grandmother's spirit, in the form of a frigate bird, flew overhead. On the journey Rata killed many monsters, including the Beast-of-Burning-Flesh and the dreaded Seven Combers, who had seven mouths, each so huge that even one could swallow Rata's canoe whole! After a long struggle with a giant clam, Rata killed the evil demon-bird, first forcing it to vomit his father's head into the basket lined with tapa *cloth.*

Rata, his weary men, and Rata's weak but grateful father sailed on until they came to evil Puna's land, the Horizon-of-the-Moon. When the wicked Puna saw the strange, dark thing that grew and grew as it drew closer, he cried out to his people, "Prepare yourselves! A giant sea-monster comes!"

The strange creature grew bigger and bigger until Puna cried, "Canoe! Look at the sail. They have killed our demon-bird! They will pay for their crime!"

Puna began to **devise** a trick. His people would build Rata the most beautiful house in all the islands of the world. The outside would be so gorgeous, the roof weaving so perfect, Rata would be unable to resist going inside it. On the poles inside would be the most **intricate** carvings ever seen by human eyes. Puna ordered his men to work day and night building the house.

ancestors
family members who came before, like great-great grandparents

pandanus
plant fiber used for weaving mats, baskets, and other products

tapa
cloth made from pounded mulberry bark

devise   invent

intricate
very detailed

209

At last, every pole and mat and beam was in place. The story of divine and human creation was carved on every pole by master carvers. The inside was filled with freshly cooked fish and the ripest fruits. Garlands of flower blossoms draped the walls. Puna sent his most beautiful daughter to invite Rata to visit the new house.

Rata's trusted helper said, "Go, my chief. But take your weapons with you. Do not trust these people."

Rata was greeted by a delicious feast. And then the dancing began. Puna's people and Rata's men spun and leaped and swayed in the firelight. What a joy to be on land again! Rata and his hosts drank cup after cup of **kava**. By dawn, everyone was falling down on sleeping mats. Puna had issued secret orders to his people: "Make our enemy dance until he is too tired to stand. He has been at sea for many days and has not left his canoe until this day. He will fall asleep. And then leave him alone." Puna broke out into an evil laugh. "The rest is up to me."

In spite of his plan to stay on his feet, never to sit down and look weak, Rata was tired. He was more tired than he had ever been in his life. Slowly, his head made fuzzy by kava, he sank to his knees. Then he lay down and closed his eyes.

Puna's people poked Rata, but he did not move. Puna's daughter came to look at him one last time. "Such a handsome young man," she whispered sadly. "I'm sorry you will die so young." She crept silently away.

Rata heard her words. Though his whole body ached for rest, just a few minutes of sleep, he stayed awake. Surely the enemy was planning a trick. How could he survive the Seven Combers and the giant clam, only to let himself fall into Puna's trap? The

kava
drink that acts like a drug

smell of smoke struck his nostrils. The thatch was on fire! Rata whispered to his spear, "Save me now!" Up into the **rafters** he heaved it. Hand over hand, Rata pulled himself up. Silently he tore a hole in the roof, and escaped into a tree.

The next morning, Puna was furious. He found no human ashes to feed to the crabs! Rata had escaped.

Rata waited to take revenge. When a roaring **typhoon** came, he set out in his canoe. Puna cackled with **glee**: "He will drown. Good riddance!" He drank kava and went to sleep happy that night.

Foolish Puna! That very night, Rata sneaked into Puna's house and plunged his spear into Puna's chest. A terrible smell rose from the wound. It was the smell of evil released and destroyed. Puna was dead at last!

Rata searched the island and finally found his mother. At Puna's cooking place, her head was buried in the dirt. Puna's wife had made her into a food stand. Heavy pineapples hung from her small feet. Her legs bowed under the weight of mangoes and breadfruits, as if the tired bones were about to break. Carefully, so carefully, Rata dug the dirt and insects from around her head. His mother's mouth was choked with sand. Blinded by her years in the dark ground, she did not recognize her own son. She knew only that a human had dug her up—in order to eat her, she thought. "You must wash me first," she whispered.

Rata heard this and understood. He wept with sorrow. "My mother, it is your son, Rata. At last I have come to take you home."

She did not believe him. "Who are you? What suffering will you bring me now?" she said. Rata sang a tender song his grandmother taught him. He

rafters
  roof supports

typhoon
  storm with very strong winds; hurricane

glee great joy

gently bathed his mother and wrapped her in fine *tapa* cloth. At last, she understood that this was no demon. These gentle hands belonged to her very own loving son.

Rata had both parents again, for the first time since he was a tiny baby. His wounded and angry heart became whole. He had learned to respect the spirits of living things, to **vanquish** his enemies, and to tame his youthful pride. He had become a man.

Rata, his parents, and all his loyal crew set out to sea one last time. The gods whipped the sea into a fury. Storm winds blew Rata's canoe back home, and then screamed and growled from horizon to horizon. The ocean twisted and thrashed as thunder shook the waves. Lightning split open the sea's dark, watery skin. The gods commanded the ocean to rise up like a mountain. The ocean obeyed, and gobbled up evil Puna's land and everything on it.

vanquish
defeat

TAHIA, THE FRAGRANT GIRL

Long ago, in a green volcanic valley on a Marquesan Island, a baby began to grow inside her mother. When this baby girl was born, before the **midwives** even washed her skin, they knew she was special. She smelled of all the flowers of their island, **Hiva Oa**. Her mother named her Tahia, the Fragrant Girl. When she was bathed, she smelled a little plainer, a little more like everyone else. Then the sweetness would grow upon her, coming from her warm, fragrant breath. Her hair smelled of plumeria, her feet of morning-flower. Even the things that came out of her body after she drank her mother's milk smelled good and sweet.

As Tahia grew, the boys of Hiva Oa came to desire her. Tahia's father, **Tuapu**, did not know about his daughter because he had left her mother before she was born. He lived in a distant valley. Even there, word reached him of a girl who smelled of flowers, of plumeria, hibiscus, and passion flower. He did not know she was his daughter. He wanted to have this fragrant girl for himself.

So one day Tuapu went to find the fragrant girl. It was the season of dryness. Yams were **shriveling** under the ground. Tahia's mother and uncles had gone to the highlands to search for food. They were gone for three days and three nights. While they

Tahia
tah HEE ah

midwives
 women who deliver babies

Hiva Oa
hee vah oh ah

Tuapu
too AH poo

shriveling
 drying up and becoming wrinkled

were gone, Tuapu found Tahia. He persuaded her to be with him the way men are with women.

When Tahia's mother Hina returned, she was very angry to learn of what had happened. She questioned her daughter. Then she said, "You **rancid** coconut!"

rancid
bad-smelling and -tasting

"Yes," answered Tahia, hanging her head in shame. Then she, too, became angry. She had not known this man was her father.

Tahia went off alone to bathe. She dried herself carefully and wove flowers into her hair. Without telling anyone, she left to find the valley where Tuapu lived.

When she reached that place, she cried, "Bad man! Come here!" Tuapu came quickly. She said angrily, "Stinking fish gut! What do you mean **seducing** your own daughter?" Tahia was so angry she pulled him all the way back to her mother's valley.

seducing
persuading to do wrong

Tuapu began to live at their house, sleeping in a room with Tahia's mother. Tahia stayed inside all the time and refused to eat. It is said that the wind was her food and the chatter of the rain her only friend. She was so sad and stayed indoors so long that her skin turned as white as coconut.

Hina's brothers were worried. They decided to find Tahia a husband. But no one pleased her. One day Tahia heard that chief **Tu Tona** was going to travel to **Nuku Hiva**. "Go, my uncles," she said. "Bring me back a husband."

Tu Tona
too TOH nah

Nuku Hiva
noo koo HEE vah

Tahia gathered flowers—gardenia, starflower, red pandanus, pink hibiscus. She scraped out a coconut and filled it with fragrant flowers and seeds. Then she asked her brother to split open another. She held it in her hand. "I turned white from grief. But I will be happy again when you find

the man whose skin is this fair," she commanded. "I will marry him."

Tahia's uncles and brothers set sail under a full moon. The wind blew its breath into the mat-sail. The people of Nuku Hiva served Tahia's kinsmen a great feast. That night the people of Nuku Hiva tattooed their bodies and danced under the full belly of the moon. Near dawn, Tahia's brothers saw something astonishing—a man as pale as milk splashed across the sand. "Get the coconut from Hiva Oa, quick!" her brother commanded. There he was, a man who looked like their sister!

"This flesh," said **Namu**, holding the coconut up to the ***poea***, "is the color of our sister's skin."

"Take me to her," pleaded the young man.

Tahia's other brother opened the coconut containing the fragrant flowers and seeds. Everyone gathered near to breathe in the heavenly scents Tahia had packed into one small coconut. Ever since that day, the sweet-smelling things from Hiva Oa have also grown on Nuku Hiva.

The next night there was a great dance on Nuku Hiva. Tahia's brothers and their new kinsman-to-be rubbed oil into their skin and dusted themselves with **turmeric**. All night they swayed and stomped their feet. "You must stop. Dawn is coming!" said her brother. "Quick, to the canoes!" They hid the *poea* under the floorboards of the canoe, where the **bilge water** gently slaps inside the hull. They sailed just after their chief climbed on board. As the sun rose, a yellow stain appeared on the bilge water.

"Look," said the bailer of bilge waters. "A dancer from Nuku Hiva must be hiding!"

Their chief pulled up the boards covering the bilge waters. Everyone was so astonished at the *poea*'s gleaming whiteness that they dropped their

Namu   nah moo

poea
   (poh EH ah)
   handsome one

turmeric
   yellow powder
   made from a
   plant; used as a
   dye or a spice

bilge water
   water that
   collects in the
   lowest point of
   a ship's inner
   hull

paddles and stared. Finally, chief Tu Tona issued a command. "Paddle on! We must go home before the storm."

When they came to Hiva Oa, the chief cried, "Tahia, Tahia! We have brought someone for you!" Tahia held an open coconut to the *poea*'s skin. Then she leaned forward and pressed noses with him. She had found her husband.

The *poea*'s people on Nuku Hiva missed him greatly, but he was happy with his new bride. Months later, he grew lonely for his parents. "I will make a quick journey to visit my parents, Tahia. Very quick," he said.

Tahia replied, "Go for one cycle of the moon only. If you leave me alone even one night longer, a terrible thing will happen. Terrible!"

"Do not worry, my love," the *poea* laughed. "I promise to return before the moon turns." He **hoisted** his sail and left for Nuku Hiva.

hoisted raised

Tahia counted the nights her husband was gone. Twenty-eight moon nights passed, but he did not return! She began weeping, weeping so hard her skirt was always wet.

When the moon began to grow again and her husband had not returned, Tahia gave up hope. She used the flesh and milk of coconuts to make her hair and skin gleam. Then she sent her uncles and brothers away to find crabs for her to eat. While they were gone, she used a rope to hang herself. The wailing from her family's hut was heard all over Hiva Oa.

After three days, Tahia's ghost went to her husband on Nuku Hiva. When he saw her in his dream, the *poea* wept and wept. He awoke and together they wept until dawn. Finally the *poea* said, "My sweetness, what are you doing here?"

"I died of grief because you did not return."

"No, no!" cried her husband. "You cannot die!"

"Oh, but I am already dead and that is that," she said softly.

"No! It can't be!" begged the *poea*.

Tahia took pity on him. "All right, then. Tell your family to gather berries and wild ginger. Scrape the flesh from many coconuts. Press all this and make a juice. And you, you must close off our room with a **tapa** curtain. After three days, they may take down the curtain."

tapa
cloth made from pounded mulberry bark

The *poea* ordered his family to follow Tahia's instructions exactly. When his family took down the *tapa* curtain after three days, fragrant Tahia was alive again. The eyes of the *poea*'s relatives were wide—how beautiful and strangely moon-like she was!

Tahia and her husband made their home on Nuku Hiva. The air around her was sweet with the scent of gardenia, passionflower, plumeria, and all the other blossoms of the island. In a month, a baby boy was growing inside her. She and her children stayed on Nuku Hiva. There Tahia lived a long, happy, and fragrant life.

MAKEMAKE AND THE BIRDS OF EASTER ISLAND

*Easter Island lies alone and with few inhabitants. Ancient stone statues suggest past glories, but no stories tell of their creation. Stories from this island deal mostly with killing and **cannibalism**. Perhaps that is why there are so few remaining islanders.*

To this day the islanders celebrate the presence of nesting birds on their island. These birds were not always here. This is their story.

On the island **Mataveri** lived many people and their gods. The people fought many wars, killing and eating one another almost without **cease**. One of the reasons they fought was to get more food. Mataveri was a small island, and it had little food. The people ate mostly fish, and it gave them a sour **disposition**!

"I wish we could taste something new. Something tasty." Over and over the people wished for change, but nothing happened.

At that time a priestess lived in a cave near the water. In this cave she kept her most precious objects. She watched them day and night. She looked for signs that would tell the future, or reduce suffering, or win the favor of a particular man or woman.

One of her most precious objects was an old

Makemake
mah keh mah keh

cannibalism
 the eating of human flesh by other humans

Mataveri
mah tah veh ree

cease   end

disposition
 mood, personality

skull. This skull had been sitting in this cave for longer than anyone knew. Perhaps it had been there at the beginning of the island itself! The priestess treasured this skull. She sensed its unusual power. She did not want anyone to take it from her.

At one time, between all of the tribal wars and fighting, there was a great storm. Huge waves rolled higher and higher. The waves were bigger than any person had ever seen. The greatest of these waves rose up over the island. As if called, the wave crashed into the priestess's cave. The wave lifted the skull and carried it far out into the sea.

The priestess saw her precious skull floating away. She tried to swim and catch it. The skull floated almost as if by magic. Whenever she got close, the skull floated faster.

It floated on and on until it reached a place right in the middle of the ocean. There it washed ashore on the island of **Matirohiva**. The priestess, using the last of her strength, collapsed on the beach just a few feet from her treasured skull.

Matirohiva
mah tee roh hee vah

When she awoke, she was surprised. A man stood looking at her. Finally he spoke. "Who are you? Why did you come to this place?"

"I am looking for my skull," she replied.

The man looked at her curiously. "That is not a skull. That is the god Makemake. I am called **Haua**, who will be a **companion** for Makemake." With that, the man tenderly lifted the skull and carried it to a special place on the island.

Haua   how ah

companion
   close friend

Once on Matirohiva, Makemake came out of the skull and took form. He and Haua were constant companions. They fished and hunted all over the island. Makemake especially enjoyed having birds to eat, for there had been no birds on the island of Mataveri.

Makemake often shared his food with the old priestess. One day she asked him," Why don't they have good food like this to eat back on our old island?"

Makemake did not know the answer to this question. He asked Haua, "Why don't you and I chase some of the birds back to Mataveri? The people there would like them. They have no birds of their own to eat."

Makemake and Haua did just that. They rounded up a whole flock of sooty terns. They drove them across the ocean to Mataveri.

Indeed the islanders were pleased. They thanked Makemake and Haua over and over. Then they ate the birds. The islanders did not use common sense. Before long all of the birds were eaten and gone. They returned to their old diet, hoping Makemake would return soon with more birds for them to eat.

A few years later, Makemake and Haua decided to check on Maraveri and see how the birds were doing. When they arrived, they could not find a single remaining bird. All the birds were gone.

Makemake was puzzled. He and Haua rounded up another large flock of terns and drove them back to Mataveri. This time he instructed the islanders to allow them to lay eggs so there would be more birds for them to eat. The islanders listened carefully.

Soon the terns built many nests, and laid many eggs. The islanders were not sure what to make of all this. One day they discovered something wonderful. The eggs were good to eat! Now the islanders thanked Makemake and Haua for both the birds and for the eggs. Then they ate them all. Every one. Every bird and every egg. Then they waited for Makemake to bring more.

"Well," said Makemake. "It has been a few years.

What say, Haua. Shall we go back to my old island and see how our birds have done?" Haua agreed. They set off at once. When Makemake and Haua arrived on Mataveri they again found no trace of any birds. Makemake questioned the people sternly, "Didn't I tell you to allow them to lay eggs?"

"Oh we did," answered the people. "And we thank you for that because they were very delicious!"

"WHAT?!" thundered Makemake. "You ATE the eggs?"

That evening, Makemake and Haua puzzled over the problem. "First they ate the birds. Then they ate the eggs. These people just don't think! They don't understand anything about birds." Haua agreed.

Then they had an idea.

Motunui
moh too noo ee

The very next day Makemake and Haua drove a third flock of sooty terns from Matirohiva. This time they did not drive the birds to Mataveri. This time they put all of the birds on **Motunui**. Motunui was an empty island just across the water from Mataveri. Here the birds could build their nests and raise their young. The men could capture and eat just a few of the birds at a time. The rest would be safe.

Even to this day there is a great celebration on Easter Island on the day the first egg of the year is discovered. The discoverer ties this egg on his head and swims with it back to Mataveri. He is honored as the "Bird Man" for that year. The rest of the eggs are left in peace.

HINA, STOLEN QUEEN

Oh she was beautiful!

And he . . . he was as handsome as he was fierce in battle. Hundreds he had killed with his own hands. Some say that at the sacrificial offerings, he heaped the slain bodies high on the altar stone shouting thanks to **Moa'ali'i**, the shark god of Moloka'i. He stacked the bodies high, yes, but not until he had eaten every left eye, swallowing many whole. He was **Kaupe'epe'e**, the king of Moloka'i.

She was Hina, the queen of Hilo, until she became his prisoner, his prize captive. To her surprise, he ruled with **compassion** and kindness. And when he spoke to her, he spoke as no one had ever before spoken. Reluctantly she answered. Reluctantly at first. He listened, truly listened. He did not pressure her to respond. She was surprised to find herself looking forward to his visits.

Their love story is a tale of romance, **reckless** love and Hawaiian **chivalry**. It is the story of Hina, Hilo's beloved queen, and Kaupe'epe'e, Moloka'i's love-crazed king.

Hina   HEE nah

Moa'ali'i moh ah ah LEE ee

Kaupe'epe'e kow peh eh PEH eh

compassion sympathy

reckless not cautious or careful
chivalry code of conduct that includes bravery, honor, and the protection of the weak

soothsayer
someone who sees into the future

Uli OO lee

sorcery
magic performed with the help of evil spirits

Hilo HEE loh

Hakalanileo
hah kah lah nee LEH oh

captivated
charmed

regal royal

penetrating
passing into or through

beckoning
calling, inviting

betrothal
engagement to be married

Hina's crossed loves were foretold by her own mother, the great **soothsayer Uli**. Uli was known throughout the islands for her powers in **sorcery** and magic. But her sorcery could not prevent what she foretold.

When Hina was yet a young maiden, the chief of **Hilo**, **Hakalanileo**, fell in love with her. He wanted her. He was **captivated** by her tall, **regal** beauty, yes, but also her mysterious presence. He could not rest, thinking of her, especially her eyes, so large and dark, so **penetrating** when her gaze met his. And always so haunting. Often Hina stood alone and silent, her face cloaked with thoughts and desires that seemed both far away but also **beckoning**, beckoning.

But Uli refused his **betrothal** gifts. Chief Hakalanileo did not give up, swearing never to leave without Hina. Uli shook her head. She liked this brave, chief, but she foresaw the tragedy that would darken their union.

The young Hilo chief begged. "I love her! I want her if only briefly she is mine. Even a few minutes together are better than this emptiness without her. Let Hina be mine!"

Uli argued but with no success. Finally she agreed to the marriage. "But I warn you. Guard Hina well! Like a great bonfire, your love will burn hot with passion. But as quickly as the spark turns to flame, the light of your life will be stolen. The winds of change blow darkly. No flame can withstand their deadly chill. Beware when night winds blow across the sea from northern islands."

Several years passed, happy years! Hina birthed two sons. Feeling content and peaceful, Hina's husband forgot Uli's warning.

But on faraway Moloka'i, Kaupe'epe'e heard the

poets sing of Hina's beauty. During a secret visit to Hilo he searched for Hina. With his own eyes he saw that the poets' songs spoke truly. Within his heart he vowed to have her. He began a reckless plan to kidnap Hina, knowing that such boldness might cost him his life and his kingdom.

One evening, in the concealment of shadows, Hina and her women went bathing as was their custom. At the beach they splashed and played. Suddenly Hina shivered. "How strange. The wind blows cool from the north tonight."

Suddenly a canoe slid into the midst of the bathers. Hands grabbed Hina, held tight, lifted her into the canoe. Soundlessly the canoe slipped back into the darkness. Over the reef it sped and was gone. Hina was gone!

On the rocky shores of Moloka'i the canoe landed. The great chief Kaupe'epe'e stood waiting. Gently he carried his captive up the steep cliffs to his **invincible** fortress, **Hā'upu**, built where the mountains hug the sea. There Hina would stay captive forever. There she would have everything she could desire, except freedom.

"Kill me or return me to my children!" she cried.

At first Kaupe'epe'e did not answer. He gazed at his prisoner, who stood proud and fierce like a true queen. She was more beautiful than he had remembered. Perhaps it was the fire of her emotions that blazed in her dark, penetrating eyes. "There is no other woman like you. Not in beauty nor in strength of heart. I am sad to refuse your request. I cannot release you. This fortress is your home until I die."

invincible
 unable to be
 conquered

Hā'upu
 HAH oo poo

"Then may we both die this very day!"

Her hateful words stirred no anger in his heart. Her **defiance** did not tempt him to strike. "Whatever might give you pleasure, just ask. It will be yours."

"Release me! I shall sorrow as long as I remain here."

"I ask only the same. Hina, I too am imprisoned—by you."

He turned and walked away. Hina ceased her **lamenting**. The longing for her sons she hid deep in her heart. She looked around and was amazed at the beauty within the fortress. Kaupe'epe'e—how unpredictable! How strange his words and gentle his voice. He had demanded nothing from her. Surprised, she found herself listening, hoping to hear his footsteps return.

Many years passed. Hina's husband in Hilo never stopped searching for his wife. Their two sons grew into manhood. Such tall, handsome warriors! They joined their father's search for their mother, Hina.

But each search proved **fruitless**. How could she have disappeared so completely?! The brothers returned to Hilo. "Before admitting defeat let us consult with our sorceress grandmother, Uli. Maybe this time she will speak to us."

For many years Uli had **mourned** for her daughter in silence. But this time when her grandsons came to her and begged for assistance, she consulted the signs of prophecy. "At last! The spirits allow me to repeat the warning given so long ago."

Her grandsons listened carefully to their grandmother's words, "Beware when night winds blow

---

defiance
challenge, opposition

lamenting
sorrowful complaining

fruitless
unsuccessful

mourned
felt sorrow over the loss of

across the sea from the northern islands."

The brothers looked at each other. "Winds from the north . . . from the north? The enemy island north of us—Moloka'i! Of course! The great fortress of Hā'upu on Moloka'i! It must be the place of our mother's imprisonment. No one has ever entered Hā'upu uninvited. No army has ever attempted attack. We must try the impossible!"

They announced their plans. Chiefs from the other Hawaiian islands agreed to assist in the attack. Great **plunder** would be theirs! Hā'upu would be **ransacked**. King Kaupe'epe'e would never be feared again.

Row after row of red war canoes paddled toward the cliffs of Moloka'i. More than twelve hundred ships were filled with warriors ready to kill:

Hā'upu! The great fortress Hā'upu! We will destroy you. Kaupe'epe'e, you will die. Your fortress will burn. Hina will be returned to Hilo at last!

Leading the charge was Hina's husband and her two warrior sons. In the very front stood Uli. She had grown old but was still strong and tough. Chanting from the front of the lead canoe she urged the men. "Row faster, row harder!" Her thin body leaned into the wind. Her long white hair flowed far behind her like the foam that flies from the surf.

Onward! Onward! Her wild war chant roared loud with excitement. The war drums *Beat - BEAT Beat - BEAT*. A constant pace: *Lift up, dip down. Pull hard! Pull hard!* Ten thousand warriors pulled oars through the ocean. Ten thousand spears pointed toward Moloka'i.

One canoe was sent ahead of the others. This canoe bore an unarmed man who carried this message: *Give us our queen. We will spare your fortress and your life.*

plunder
  items taken by force

ransacked
  serarched thoroughly and stolen from

Kaupe'epe'e replied. "Your queen resides happily within Hā'upu's walls. She is mine. I desire no life without her."

The drums beat faster. The war canoes sped more quickly toward Moloka'i.

Meanwhile, at Hā'upu, Kaupe'epe'e had not stood idle. Every movement of the enemy had been watched and reported. Every inch of the mighty stone fortress was filled with warriors. Young men shouted war chants as they gathered **provisions** and prepared weapons—spears, stones, axes, and clubs. Kaupe'epe'e's army was outnumbered ten to one, but they had the protection of the mighty walls of Hā'upu and provisions and weapons to fight for months.

provisions
food and other supplies

Kaupe'epe'e's plan of counterattack was ready. He anticipated that the enemy canoes would land on the one narrow beach. This beach bordered a steep gully up which warriors could climb. A dam of boulders had been piled at the top of this gully.

Standing on the wall nearest the sea, Kaupe'epe'e watched the canoes land by the hundreds. "Yes, I have foreseen correctly. Now the Hilo warriors will wait until darkness. By the thousands they will climb upward." Kaupe'epe'e looked at his own warriors. To their surprise, he looked at them sadly. "We are gravely outnumbered. Many will die; few will live. Any of you who wish to be alive after this day, I grant you pardon and permission. Leave! Once the battle has begun, only your blood is assured of escape."

Not one warrior left. They stood silently within the fortress, waiting, listening. The sky streaked purple and red as the sun set. The whole world seemed hushed. Like a heavy **shroud**, night's darkness closed in around the fortress. Suddenly,

shroud
covering for a dead body

shouts and war cries echoed up the **gorge,** at first distantly then louder, louder!

"Begin the fight! Open the dam of destruction!"

The wall of rock was let loose. Down rolled an avalanche of boulders, down over the enemy warriors. A stream of destruction suffocated and swept away everything alive. War cries became death screams. The cliffs shook as if earthquakes were splitting open the island. The **gully** turned black and slippery with blood and crushed bodies.

Kaupe'epe'e won the first round of battle.

The sea army from Hilo retreated. But what Kaupe'epe'e did not know was that a rear assault had also begun. A human wall of Hilo warriors lined the mountaintops **flanking** the fortress. No reinforcements or supplies could pierce this line. Behind this wall, men skilled in weaponry worked without rest to construct a movable monstrous shield. Whole tree trunks reaching twenty feet in height were tied together with cords. At the top of every fourth timber was **lashed** a movable brace. When this giant shield was raised, the men behind it were safe from the spears, rocks and arrows slung from the fortress. Every night during the safety of darkness, this giant shield was advanced a few yards forward. Night after night, Hilo's army moved closer to Hā'upu, the fortress once thought invincible.

The warriors of Hā'upu stood defiantly on top of Hā'upu's walls, spears aimed at the attacking army. But their weapons were powerless. Nothing they threw had any effect. Not one spear hurled at the enemy penetrated the giant wooden shield.

Finally, storm clouds piled thick and swirled

gorge
narrow passage through land

gully
trench formed by running water

flanking
on each side of

lashed
tied with cords

black. Day became night. A cold wind blew first from one side then another. Rain fell hard and blinding as a waterfall. It was no night for battle, so thought Kaupeʻepeʻe and his men. Leaving only a few guards, his warriors retreated to dry quarters within the fortress.

During this cover of darkness, Hilo's army advanced. Step by silent step they pushed their timbered shield until it touched the very walls of Hāʻupu. The battle charge began! Hilo warriors swarmed up by the hundreds. Like an avalanche of bodies, they hurled themselves over the walls into the fortress. Cries of alarm and warning screamed from within. Too late! A **cataract** of spears was thrown. Battle and bloodshed had begun.

cataract
  downpour, flood

Like a wave of destruction, spears, warriors, battle-axes swept through Hāʻupu. Shouts of victory mixed with screams of dying. The moaning of the wounded was lost in the tramping and stomping of rushing warriors. Blood covered the stone floor like water and dripped from the **terraced** gardens.

terraced
  built on a series of levels, like stair steps

bowels
  deepest parts

heiau
  (heh ee ow) temple

The sons of Hina led the advancing troops. Farther and farther into the **bowels** of the fortress they marched. Over the highest terraces and across the sacred *heiau*, they advanced their troops. Finally, in front of the temple they encountered Kaupeʻepeʻe. All his remaining warriors, less than fifty, stood ready to defend him.

The final battle was brief. A spear pierced the breast of Kaupeʻepeʻe. He stood bleeding, poised to hurl his own weapon at the attacking chief. As this young chief turned toward him, Kaupeʻepeʻe recognized the handsome face. It was Hina's son.

"For her sake, you live as I die. Honor your queen mother!"

With those words Kaupeʻepeʻe fell lifeless.

Hidden within the temple, Hina was found safe and unharmed.

The walls of the fortress Hā'upu were savagely torn down until not one stone remained on another. Kaupe'epe'e's body was recovered. A royal burial was performed with respect and honor. His bones lie hidden on his beloved Moloka'i. Perhaps his spirit rests near the very place where he had imprisoned Hina, his beloved queen.

Hina returned to Hilo, where she lived with her husband and sons, living as she had always lived, a true queen in pride and grace. Often she would stand alone watching the tossing waters of the sea. Her eyes seemed to smile when winds from the north blew gently across her face.

THE BLOOD, THE PROMISE, AND THE TATTOO

Mataora
mah tah OH rah

parched very dry

Niwareka
nee vah REH kah

Uetonga
oo eh TAWNG ah

embedded
placed so as to become a part of the surrounding material

soot
fine black powder produced by burning

moko   moh koh

adorned decorated

Mataora's face was swollen and bloody. It was so swollen, he could not swallow. But his **parched** throat cried for water. Water! Just as his sad heart cried for his lost love, **Niwareka**. If he survived this torture of receiving the tattoo, then surely he would have the courage to find his wife, Niwareka, daughter of the underworld. If he found her, would she forgive him?

As Mataora lay flat on his back, the tattoo master, **Uetonga**, continued the peck, peck, pecking of his bone needle, piercing Mata's forehead. Piece by piece the needle broke new skin and **embedded** black dye made from shark oil and **soot**. Cut by cut the lizard lines covered Mata's face, making the tattoo, the *moko*. This tattoo would never come off.

Already, tattoo lines curved around and around his cheeks and chin. The mark of the lizard **adorned** his forehead and nose. Strange lines as crooked as lizard's legs spiraled away from his nose. Yes, he, Mata of the human world, must endure this ritual and prove he had enough courage to be a worthy husband. Then, too, he would be handsome with tattoo. Perhaps then Niwareka would forgive him. The pain of the tattoo would teach him never to cause her pain again.

Mata clenched his hands, his knuckles white

and his arms trembling. Peck, peck, peck, continued the tattoo needle. Dry, dry, dry. Mata's throat burned hot as fire. His head throbbed and ached as if his brain were about to explode. Water! He must drink soon or die!

But his lips were swollen full and fat like a puffer fish. He could not open them to sip from the coconut shell. His arms no longer had strength to reach for water nor beg for help. Losing Niwareka had meant losing so much. He must find her!

His head was spinning and his thoughts felt tangled like a fishing line. The pain was muddying his memory. Why had he come here? Why had he, Mataora, the proud **Maori** chief, traveled to this cursed underworld? This was a dreaded place where only spirits of the dead and **Turehu** fairy women lived. These strange but lovely, graceful women had pale skin, light eyes, and golden hair flowing to the ground like spun sunlight. Niwareka! He was searching for his beloved Niwareka.

Maori
MAH oh ree

Turehu
too REH hoo

In whispered words, he began the sad song that had given him hope during his long journey. He sang of his search for the beautiful maiden who had agreed to become his wife. He sang joyously of their happiness. Yes! Then, sadly, he sang of his jealousy, his foolish anger, an anger that had caused him to strike the very one he treasured.

Salty tears stung his bloody face like lines of fire. Fire of passion. Jealousy. He had struck her, beaten her. His beloved Niwareka. Thus he sang:

I search for you asking for forgiveness, Niwareka. I have followed your own tearful trail to your home of darkness. Niwareka! If you hear me, pause and listen. Listen to my song of sorrow. Never again will I harm you. Niwareka, Niwareka! The pain of the tattoo has taught me, strengthened me. Niwareka, forgive me.

The daughters of Uetonga, the tattoo master, heard his singing. They listened to his sad story. They heard this warrior from above repeating their sister's name. *We must tell her! Niwareka, our sister who returned home weeping. Weeping for her beloved. Weeping for her loss. Why had he hurt her, he who* **vowed** *to* **cherish** *and love her?*

Quickly the daughters of the tattoo master ran to their sister.

Niwareka ceased her weeping. She walked to the tattoo house, her father's house, to see this man who sang her name. "Surely this could not be Mata, my husband. Surely no human man, not even a brave Maori warrior, would step into **Rarohenga**, the spirit world of darkness."

She gazed at his face, the one who lay moaning and singing. His eyes could not open because of the swelling. She touched his eyelids. Gently, gently she stopped the tears that flowed down his bleeding face. Her own tears fell on his lips. "Mata, it is I for whom you sing. Mata!"

"Niwareka," he whispered. "Forgive me."

Drop by drop she gave him water to swallow.

Pound, pound, pound. Niwareka cooked and then smashed taro and breadfruit. Using her father's clay funnel she fed her beloved. Day after day she sang with her sisters. They sang to soothe the pain of the *moko*.

Lizard tails swirled around Mata's cheeks. Lizard legs curved over each eyebrow. Peck-peck-peck, and then the tattoo was finished. With time the bleeding stopped, the swelling **receded**. Mata's face healed.

vowed promised

cherish
    care for lovingly

Rarohenga
rah roh HENG ah

receded grew less

Niwa's own sorrow still ached in her heart. She gazed at her husband. Had he learned from his pain? "The ways of your people are wicked and strange," she told him. "To hurt one another, this we cannot even imagine." Niwareka stared at her husband. "A man must never beat his woman."

Uetonga, her father, spoke now to Mata. "I feel your impatience, your desire to return with my daughter. Leave her here. Our dark world is gentle. Family does not strike family. Leave her here."

Mata hung his head in shame. "Let her come. I have learned. I will hold back my anger. My hand shall not strike her again."

Uetonga stared at the man warrior. "The tattoo I have given you will never come off." Uetonga looked a long while at Mata. "Will your words last like the lizard on your face?"

"I give my promise. I have learned."

Uetonga looked at his daughter and then again at Mata. "Our *moko* does not wash off like the warrior's face paint. Wear our tattoo with honor. And with honor, remember your promise."

Niwareka returned with her warrior husband to his world of light, **Te Aoturoa**. As a gift of parting, Uetonga gave Mata a treasured **cloak** called **Rangihaupapa**, the cloak from which all others on earth would be designed. He gave this cloak with one warning. "As you leave our darkness, tell the gatekeeper of this treasure. Conceal nothing. Tell the truth."

But in his impatience to leave the dark world, Mata forgot.

When the gatekeeper discovered the hidden

Te Aoturoa
teh ah oh too ROH ah

cloak   cape

Rangihaupapa
rahng ee how PAH pah

cloak, he cursed the warrior. "Never again can people return to the underworld. Never until death! Go! Take with you the owl, the bat and the **kiwi**. Take them as guides. But in your world, they shall hide in the darkness. Night's black cloak will offer them safety."

kiwi
flightless bird
with a long bill

With the help of the owl, the bat, and the kiwi, Mata and Niwareka returned to the light world. Because of Mata's forgetfulness, people cannot return to the spirit world until after death. But because of his courage, people have the art of tattoo, *moko*. Sons learn from fathers and then teach their sons.

Moko, the art of tattoo: see the lines of the lizard on the face of the warriors. Lizard legs, tail twitching, stretch over the eyes. Circles curve from the nostrils and the mouth down to the chin. Swirling spirals **flare** over the nose to crown the high cheekbones.

flare
spread outward

Warriors—your faces bloody and your lips swollen—remember the *moko*! Mata's promise! Have courage, care for one another. Remember!

236

AUSTRALIA

The **Aborigines** of Australia have many creation stories. In one, an evil son thrust a spear into his spirit-father. The father was terribly hurt. Blood poured from him as he dragged himself across the land. Everywhere his blood spilled, freshwater pools formed. Rocks cracked open and cool streams poured out. He knew he was dying. As he dragged himself along, he gathered all the fire in the world. He used his hair to tie the fire onto his head. Then he waded out into the sea. He was going to put out all the fires! Just as he was about to dive under the water, a man grabbed one fiery stick from his head. Fire was saved for all people! What if there had been no brave man to snatch the burning stick? In another story, an accidental fire leads to the creation of the sun. You can read about that fire in the story "The Sky Spirits Create the Sun." It and other aboriginal legends explain the relationship of nature, people, and spirits on the island continent of Australia.

Australia is the oldest continent in the world.

aborigines
first people to live in a region

Some of its rock is over four billion years old. Rain and winds have beaten down its mountains. Today it is mainly flat, hot, dry desert. The land is often red or gold or the brown-gold of a lion's fur. It has been described as looking like dirty rust. Imagine **images** painted on the desert rocks of Australia. These are the Mimi people: tiny people shaped like thin sticks. Some people see only painted images on a rock. But the Aborigines of Australia see the Mimi people come alive. These spirit people show themselves when it is very quiet. And they show themselves only to people who understand their special power.

images drawings

Not all of Australia is desert. In between the Eastern coast and the deserts are highlands, the Great Dividing Range. Still, most of Australia receives less than twenty inches of rain a year. Around its edges, though, Australia is a wetter and more comfortable place to live.

Australia is a big country, especially compared with Pacific islands. It has over three million square miles of land. Long ago, Australia is thought to have been part of two supercontinents, **Pangaea** and **Gondwana**. For 35 million years, Australia has been a separate continent. But now the sea floor of the Indian Ocean is spreading. Australia is drifting northward toward Asia. When more time has passed, Australia will join Asia, as India did. Then there will be no such place as the continent of Australia.

Pangaea
pan JEE uh

Gondwana
gahn DWAHN uh

SETTLEMENT AND HISTORY

The Aborigines migrated from Asia over sixty thousand years ago. Some scientists believe there was a land bridge between Asia and Australia then. The **ancestors** of today's Aborigines may have

ancestors
family members who came before, like great-great grandparents

walked all the way from Asia to Australia. They were hunters and gatherers. They lived a **nomadic** life, looking for food. They camped in the bush, or Outback. Families traveled together. Sometimes groups of families came together briefly.

Before Europeans came, there may have been around 300,000 Aborigines. They took what they needed from the surface of the land. They had a habit of burning it over and over. Why did they do this? Perhaps to let new plants grow. Some scientists think this burning caused most of the large animals to become **extinct**. Today, Australia has unusual native plants and animals. There are many kinds of eucalyptus trees. Australia's deserts, grasslands, and tropical rain forests are home to tree kangaroos, **wallabies**, **koalas**, and mountain pygmy possums. Unlike on Pacific islands, there are large animals: the giant **wombat** and the **marsupial** lion. A species of saltwater crocodile is known to eat humans. There are also poisonous snakes. The **dingo** is thought to have been brought by Aborigines. The legend "How the Kangaroo Got Her Pouch" tells how a kind-hearted kangaroo mother was rewarded by a wombat who was actually a god in disguise.

In the north, people traditionally made shelters from bark. During monsoon season, they lived in caves or houses on stilts to protect themselves from rain and mosquitoes. In the desert, they made windbreaks to protect themselves from wind and blowing sand.

Aborigines slept out under the stars. They also liked to go naked. For most of their history, they felt clothing was unnecessary. It separated them from nature and the spirit of creation. As in the Pacific Islands, these traditional practices have changed somewhat.

nomadic
moving from place to place

extinct
no longer existing

wallabies
small or medium-sized kangaroos

koalas
small marsupials that feed on eucalyptus leaves

wombat
stocky marsupial

marsupial
animal with a pouch for its young

dingo   wild dog

Aboriginal women often carried heavy loads on their heads. They used grass cushions to soften the load and balance it well. The men carried spears and sometimes **boomerangs**. Women had digging sticks and deep wooden bowls. They used the bowls to hold water, food, and even their babies. Men were often hunters. Women were often vegetable gatherers. As in the Pacific Islands, it was considered wrong to be selfish. Aboriginal children were taught to help their families.

In ancient times, Asians may have visited Australia. Later, Spanish and Portuguese explorers sailed by. In 1788, the British Royal Navy arrived from England. Soon, they established colonies. Some of them were **penal** colonies. The British brought in prisoners no one wanted in England. In the 1800s, the immigrant population increased and the Aboriginal population decreased.

In the beginning, the two groups didn't understand each other. The Aboriginal people have brown skins of many different shades. Most have curly hair. The settlers from Europe were nearly all pale-skinned. The spiritual beliefs of the two groups were also very different. So were their ways of life. The Europeans did a great deal of harm to the Aborigines. They fought with them, killing many of them. When Aborigines worked for Europeans, they were not always well treated. The Europeans also brought diseases that killed Aborigines quickly. Some Aborigines came to believe that they would all die. Eventually, the Europeans forced many Aborigines onto small pieces of land. These were called "reserves." Because Aborigines are nomadic, many cannot live happily on a tiny piece of land. At one time, Aboriginal children were taken from their parents. They were forced to live as orphans or with white families. This is no longer the case.

There are few Aborigines today. A few years ago, less than two percent of Australians were Aborigines. Almost none have pure Aboriginal blood. A few Aborigines still maintain tribal life in the Outback. But most now live on the outskirts of cities. Many are poor. Their babies die more often than those of European descent. They have more trouble with disease. They often receive less education.

Today, much of the land that once belonged to the Aborigines is used for sheep-raising and mining. The Aborigines have fought the government to try to get their land back. However, much of it is lost to them forever.

In 1901, the colonies became six states and two territories: Victoria, New South Wales, Queensland, Western Australia, South Australia, Tasmania, Australian Capital Territory, and Northern Territory. Tasmania was once part of mainland Australia. But water flooded the Bass Strait, perhaps twelve thousand years ago. Now the two places are separated.

Australia is an independent nation with a constitution and an elected parliamentary government. But most Australians consider the Queen of England to be Australia's queen, too. However, some Australians don't want a foreign queen.

ABORIGINAL SPIRITUAL BELIEFS

For the Aboriginal people, the world was created during the "Dreaming," or "Dreamtime." This idea includes all of time. The past exists in the present. The Dreaming isn't a place. It is a deeply spiritual state of being. Even today some Aborigines know how to enter into it. In the Dreaming, mythic beings created all things.

What was the world like before the Dreaming? It was a flat, endless plain. The spirits of people had no arms or legs. They couldn't talk or eat or feel. The sky spirits came to earth and created all its features. Everything we know—every mountain and stream and tree and person—is like a picture drawn by a sky spirit. It might even be a picture of his or her face. Another way to think of it is that Nature is like a language. Each thing we see is a different word.

For the Aborigine, the world is perfect and does not need change. In fact, if it is changed, the story it needs to tell may be interrupted. The mythic beings of the past taught people how to understand the world. There are rules for creation and rules for how to live on the land. Ceremonies must be performed in order to ensure the survival of the world. The land itself is a map of the creation of the Dreaming. Europeans, however, often disagree. This difference of feeling about the land has caused suffering among Aborigines.

Aborigine culture today has some things in common with Pacific Island culture. Clans are important. Marriage is not just between two people. It is a relationship between two families. Traditionally, some children were promised in marriage when they were still babies. Some men had more than one wife. There was love magic and **elopement**. If you were a man, you could even capture the woman you wanted to marry.

When Aboriginal children are born, their spirits come from the Dreaming. Most people have a **totem** animal. It might be a bird or a dingo. Aborigines say that their flesh is the same as their totem animal's flesh. They know they should not eat their totem animal, even if it is delicious. Their mother is the one who knows which totem is theirs. She knows

elopement
running off secretly with the person you want to marry

totem
representative of the clan, or family

which spirit-children chose her body.

Traditionally, Aboriginal boys had special ceremonies to celebrate their manhood. These ceremonies might take place when the boys were between six and sixteen years old. They included **circumcision**, nose-bone piercing, bloodletting, and scar-making. Sometimes the boys were "killed" in a ceremony, in order to become adult men. Girls had their own ceremonies: they were separated from other people. They had to observe special food **taboos**. In this way, boys and girls gained spiritual power.

Aborigines believe they must honor the law of the Dreaming. If they don't, children may not be born. The world may not continue. They obey the rules they have learned from their elders. They enact important ceremonies. Some of these involve long, **sacred** songs or stories. When many people gather to hear songs, the event is sometimes called a *corroboree*. Aborigines make music with the *didgeridoo* and clapping sticks. The main subject of their myths is the land—how it came to be, why parts of it are sacred. Seasons are linked to the land: there is the cool time, the rainy time, the sunny time. There is also the grasshopper time, when yams are ready to be dug up. In the singing-lizard time, people come together in the Outback to chant and dance.

Some adults go on Walkabout, a personal spiritual journey. Often they go alone. They do not go until they are spiritually mature. As they travel, they name each place. They go long distances, perhaps a thousand miles. Therefore, their feet are very important to them. They may tell stories by drawing in the sand or through dance. When they dance, their feet pound the earth. They are speaking to the earth. They listen for a response.

circumcision
removal of the foreskin of the penis

taboos
things that are forbidden

sacred
worthy of respect

corroboree
caw rob uh REE

didgeridoo
(didj uh ree DOO) wooden trumpet

On Walkabout, they tell the story of the earth's creation and its ties to ancestral beings. The story explains where important things are. Sacred places are often thought of as "hot" because they are full of spirit-energy. Hot sites include water holes, caves, and dangerous places it is best to avoid.

Once, there was a **karadji** who saved his people from drought. There was so little rain that his people had nothing to eat. He found a mountain with foot-holes cut into the rock. For days, he climbed the rock ladder. At last he found water to drink. He rested, and then he saw circles formed out of stones. He entered one of the circles. The roaring voice of a sky spirit filled his ears! The *karadji* begged for water for his people. Then he felt himself lifted into the sky. The spirit ordered him to gather flowers and return to his tribe.

Down in the desert below, the drought ended. This holy man had known how to contact the spirits of the Dreaming. Nature and spirit were in harmony again. This is what Aborigines of Australia wish for—the return of harmony among spirit, nature, and humans.

karadji
(kuh RAHJ ee)
Aborigine with special spiritual knowledge

THE SKY SPIRITS CREATE THE SUN

Long, long ago, there was a moon and stars, but no sun. No warmth or light. Until one day, **Dinewan**, the emu, a large walking bird, and her friend **Brolga**, the crane, had a fight. Brolga was so angry she grabbed an egg from Dinewan's nest. The egg was huge, but Brolga was made strong by her fury. She threw the egg with all her might up into the sky! Poor Dinewan saw her egg smash against a giant pile of firewood. High, high, in the sky, the shell shattered. As the yellow yolk splashed across the wood, it burst into flame!

Down below, everything lit up. Never had the animals seen such a fine light. They had been living in twilight, the darkness of moon and stars. Now they were amazed at the light.

A spirit in the sky saw that the earth was beautiful now. It was bathed in warm, golden light. Why not have a fire every day? Ever since the day Brolga threw the egg, the spirit has kept the **embers** of that first fire alive. At night, the spirit and his helpers gather firewood. "Pile the wood high!" he orders. "Morning star, uncover your face and let your light spill forth. Spin and twirl! Make them see you down below." When the morning star twinkles, the creatures on earth know the sun will soon appear. The spirit then takes a torch and lights the sun-fire for another

Dinewan
dihn uh wahn
Brolga   brawl guh

embers
   glowing remains
   of a fire

245

day. Small flames lick the wood, growing bigger, bigger, bursting into a glowing ball of fire.

But long ago some creatures on earth paid no attention. They slept through the dance of the morning star. Some crawled into caves to avoid the dawn. Others turned over and continued to snore. The sky spirits thought they were rude—they didn't appreciate these precious gifts. So the sky spirits decided to make noise. A huge noise that no one— NO ONE—could sleep through.

They searched for a long time to find the right noise. It had to be deep and full and unforgettable. They listened to many creatures, both **divine** and earthly, make their loudest noises. Coughing, hiccupping, stomping, crying. But not one was the right one.

divine like a god

One evening when they were visiting the great desert below, they heard the **Googoorgaga** laugh. He is a laughing **jackass** who makes a sound no one could ever forget. It sounds like "Reeeeeeehh-haaaaoonnngh." Only it shakes the earth, forces eyelids to open, and steals the yawns from inside the sleepers' mouths.

Googoorgaga
goo goor GAH gah

jackass
  male donkey

"That's it," they said. "We want his voice forever and ever."

And so, as the morning star fades, the Googoorgaga laughs his loudest laugh. At first, he didn't want to. But when the spirits told him he must agree, or the sun-fire would not be lit, he changed his mind. He did not want to be remembered as the creature too stingy to provide the earth with light. Thanks to him, we have light and warmth.

In the morning, the firewood burns slowly. But as the day goes on, every stick and every log catches fire. By the middle of the day, the fire is blazing. It is so hot that earth creatures crawl into the shade.

By evening, the fire is only glowing embers. The spirits cover the embers with clouds. They save them for dawn, when they use them to light the new pile of wood.

Human children are not allowed to laugh like the Googoorgaga. If they do, he may feel insulted. For his is not a pretty laugh! And if he gets angry and refuses to laugh any more, the fire will go out forever.

Every once in a while a child does laugh the Googoorgaga's laugh. It's hard not to want to try it at least once. But be careful! If you do, you will grow an extra tooth in a strange part of your mouth. Everyone who sees it will know why it grew there!

HOW THE KANGAROO GOT HER POUCH

joey baby

wombat
stocky
Australian
marsupial
(animal with a
pouch for its
young) that
looks like a
small bear

veered
changed
direction

Long ago, the kangaroo was grooming her **joey** on the bank of a brook. They liked to listen to the water burble as the mama combed her baby's fur. On this day, an old **wombat** staggered toward them.

"Oh dear," the kangaroo whispered to her baby. "This wombat is old and sick. He must have great-great-grandchildren already."

The mother kangaroo thought she heard the sound of weeping. As the wombat **veered** closer, she heard him say, "Useless and worthless, worthless and useless."

"What's the trouble, friend wombat?" she said.

"Huh?" he said, startled. "Who said that?"

"I did," said the kangaroo. "A kangaroo and her joey."

"I'm blind," the wombat replied. "Nobody wants me around. Nobody thinks about me. I'm no good any more. They've abandoned me, all of them."

The kangaroo, who had a tender heart, said, "It's not as bad as all that. I'll be your friend. My joey and I will show you where the tastiest grass grows." She let the wombat hold her tail. Then, slowly, she led him over to the juiciest grass and cleanest water. The old wombat sighed with pleasure. It made the kangaroo happy to see him feeling better.

Suddenly she remembered her joey! She had

told him to stay close, but he had wandered off again. She raced back to look for him. So many times this had happened. She'd look for food, and when she looked up, he had wandered off. It scared her terribly.

She found her joey asleep under a gum tree. Not wanting to wake him from his nap, she decided to go back and check on the old wombat. Something was moving in the bush. An **Aboriginal** hunter, silently stalking the wombat! Already his boomerang was raised above his head, its smooth edges ready to slice the air. The kangaroo froze. She couldn't even breathe. She wanted to run, but the wombat was like her joey— she had to protect him!

The kangaroo began to stomp on the branches and twigs under her feet. Thump, thump, crack, crack, she pounded the earth. The hunter turned toward her. "Run," she screamed to the wombat, "Run! There's a hunter." The wombat took off crazily, not knowing where he was going. The hunter didn't care. Now all he wanted was the kangaroo!

She hopped as fast and hard as she could into the bush, away, away from where she had left her joey asleep. Her heart thumped wildly in her throat as she ran for her life. At last she came to a cave. She was too tired to go farther, and collapsed on the dirt floor inside. At least he would have to kill her in the cool dark, not out in the open where other animals would be forced to watch.

The hunter ran past the mouth of the cave! The kangaroo stayed inside, listening for his return. She was afraid to go out. Finally, she saw him walk past the mouth of the cave again, his boomerang hanging from his hand. She waited until it was safe, then ran as fast as she could back to the gum tree. There was her joey, awake and ready to play. Together they

went to look for the wombat, but he had gone.

What the kangaroo mother didn't know was that the wombat wasn't a wombat. He was actually the great god **Byamee** who had put on a disguise. Byamee had descended from the sky world to find out which of his creatures had the kindest heart. Now he had an answer that pleased him greatly: the kangaroo. Byamee wanted to give her the gift that would help her most of all. So he called the sky spirits together and said, "Go down below to where the eucalyptus grow tall. Peel the long strips of bark and make a **dilly bag** apron. Give it to the kangaroo mother and explain that she must tie it around her waist."

And so they did. At the very moment the kangaroo mother tied the apron around her waist, Byamee transformed it into soft kangaroo fur. It grew into her own flesh. Now she had a pouch in which to carry her baby joey. He could even sleep in there as she went about her daily tasks.

The kangaroo mother was very happy with her gift. But because she was the kindest creature of all, she didn't want to keep it only for herself. She thought about the other kangaroo mothers and about the **wallaby** mothers and the kangaroo rats and all the other marsupials.

Byamee loved the kangaroo's generous heart. So he decided to make pouches for all the other marsupial mothers. Ever since then, their babies almost never get lost.

Byamee
bye ah mee

dilly bag
loosely woven bag made of native fibers

wallaby
small or medium-sized kangaroo

NERIDA AND BIRWAIN: A LOVE STORY

Nerida
neh REE dah

Birwain bur wayn

murk   darkness

mussels
   type of shellfish

Wahwee
wah wee

grief   sorrow

initiation rites
   ceremonies to
   admit to
   membership or
   mark the
   beginning of

While the sun gave the stars and moon their rest, a girl and a boy met every day by a water hole. The hole was deep and dark, its bottom lost in **murk**. The girl, Nerida, and her friend, Birwain, loved to dig for **mussels** at the edge of the hole. Often they heard the distant rumble of thunder.

Nerida and Birwain loved to be together at the water hole. They didn't know that the thunder was the angry voice of the water spirit, **Wahwee**. Or that they were digging at Wahwee's private water hole and he was plotting revenge. When the thunder roared so loudly it hurt their ears, they would run home to their mothers. But not without taking the biggest and best mussels, found only at that hole.

The two friends didn't know that Wahwee had once caused a huge flood to drown the world. That only a few people had survived. That a **grief**-cry had filled the sky-dome. Everyone knew not to go near Wahwee's water hole. Everyone but Nerida and Birwain.

Wahwee hid in the murky water and spied on Nerida and Birwain. Day by day, they were growing older. Nerida was turning into a lovely young woman. She and Birwain were falling in love. Birwain would soon undergo **initiation rites** into manhood. Then he would be able to ask Nerida's family for permission to live with her.

Wahwee was jealous. He wanted the lovely Nerida for himself. In the dark hours of the night, he plotted how he would steal her. Foolish Nerida and Birwain. They wanted to be alone, away from all the eyes of the world. Little did they know that Wahwee was watching with **bulging** eyes as round as **gourds**!

One day, Nerida reached the water hole before Birwain. As she sat at the water's edge, cooling her feet, an old woman came by. The woman was weeping so hard the tears ran in streams down her cheeks. Nerida felt sorry for her. She offered her the warm cooked yams she had made for Birwain.

"**Bargie**," she said, using the name that means "grandmother," "have a yam. It will comfort you."

"Oh no," said the woman. "I am not hungry. I am terribly sad. Your whole tribe will be killed because of you. Because of your and your lover Birwain's ignorance."

Nerida **shuddered**. Who was this old woman? How did she know Birwain's name? It was a secret that she loved Birwain. What terrible destruction could she mean? For a time, they sat in silence. Nerida's ears did not want to hear, but she knew they must.

"Bargie, what do you mean? How have I caused anyone harm?"

"Over and over again, you have stolen from Wahwee, the water spirit. He is angry. Every single mussel you cooked and ate was an insult to him. Did you not hear the thunder rumbling in the sky? But you did nothing. Then it turned to a roar, and still you did nothing. Even as the earth shook, nearly uprooting the yams, you and Birwain continued to steal!"

Nerida trembled at these words. Were they true?

bulging
sticking out, swollen

gourds
hard-shelled fruits used to make containers

Bargie   bahr jee

shuddered
shook with fear

"Your tribe is innocent, but they will all die with you. You and Birwain are the guilty ones." She paused, and her voice softened. "I see your kind heart. You offered to share food. Too bad I can't save you."

"Dear Bargie, I am willing to die," said Nerida. "But you must save the innocent people of my tribe. Save Birwain. I will gladly die to save all of them."

"It's not that easy. Birwain stole too. He must suffer as you will suffer," said the old woman.

"Please, kind Bargie. Please save Birwain," begged Nerida.

"Come tomorrow. Alone. I will see if anything can be done. Feel the water trembling at your feet. Wahwee is boiling down below. Once he flooded the world and he has promised to do it again. We will all drown and float dead upon the waters that will cover the world. I will tell him you are willing to sacrifice your life to make **amends**. Come tomorrow and we will see."

amends
something done or paid to apologize

The old woman turned into a black, slippery eel. Nerida gasped as it slid into the murky water hole. A witch! She had been tricked. She ran home without waiting for Birwain. Even as she ran, she wept. Today would be her last day alive.

The next day she returned to the water hole. How horrible the old woman looked to her. But there was no choice. "Bargie," Nerida said, trying to keep her voice from trembling, "can we save my people and save Birwain?"

"We will see. The only chance is for you to follow me into the water hole. I will dive down deep and you must follow without **hesitation**. Wahwee says you must ask his forgiveness. He is ready to unleash the storm of all storms. His voice will cause the clouds to **collide**. Thunder will break over the land.

hesitation
slowness to act

collide
crash together

254

His brothers the rain and winds will rage, knocking down trees. The birds will drown, the fish will drift unconscious among the coral. People will cling to their houses, but the houses will float away. Babies will drown. And then everyone else will die.

"Stop it, stop it!" cried Nerida. "Let us go. I am ready now." She knew the old woman was a witch, but there was no choice. Nerida stared at the **roiling** black water before her. A wicked smile curled on the old woman's lip. She had stolen Nerida from Birwain!

The old woman **writhed** and cried out. Her back grew dark and slimy. She became a slippery eel, sliding under the water's dirty surface. Nerida looked at the sky, already darkening with Wahwee's rage, and prayed for the safety of Birwain and all people. Then she gulped air and plunged into the water.

From the forest, Birwain saw a splash. He ran to the pool, but now there were only quiet circles spreading on its surface. He found Nerida's tracks leading to the pool's edge. There they disappeared. Birwain howled with grief. Then he ran home to get his people to help him. "Wahwee, the water spirit, has her now," they said. "There is nothing to be done. If only we had known. It is strictly forbidden to go to that pool!"

Birwain could think only of how to get Nerida back. Perhaps she wasn't dead yet. "I love her more than my life," he said to his tribe. "Wahwee **lured** her into the water. I will bring her back with the power of my love."

Every day after that, Birwain sat where Nerida's footprints disappeared into the water. Every day he chanted a love song:

roiling
stirred up, violently moving

writhed
twisted as if in pain

lured
attracted by offering something

255

Nerida, Nerida, I wait for you
Love of all time, love of my life,
I wait for you. Here on the bank
Where we fished together, I wait.

Nerida, Nerida, there is no one but you,
Come back, my Nerida, I'll lift you up.
My arms are strong for you, Nerida.
Hear my song; come, Nerida, come.

For many months Birwain sang. He didn't even
notice when the greedy Wahwee poured rain on
him. His tribe believed he had gone crazy. They
brought him food because he would not leave the
pond. But they knew he was lost to them forever,
caught in Wahwee's web.

One day Birwain saw the water move. A green
leaf the size of a woman's hand rose above its surface.
Gently, it opened and spread, like fingers stretching
in the sun. The next day another leaf appeared
beside it. Birwain sang on. A flower bud unfolded
next to the leaves, the face of a red water lily. He
stared and stared at this unfolding beauty. Then he
recognized her—the curving lip where the petals
joined the stem.

He leaped to his feet and cried out, "Nerida! At
last, you have come back. I am coming, my love."
Birwain plunged into the dark water. He kicked in
great thrusts to keep his head above water. More
than anything he wanted to touch the delicate red
lily, his precious Nerida.

Jealous Wahwee was watching! Just as Birwain
clasped Nerida's face between his hands, Wahwee
pulled him under the water, down, down, to the
murky bottom of the pool. A huge and heavy weight
held him by the legs and sucked him down. As his

head went under, he let go of his flower Nerida. Thrashing in the roiling water, he began to choke. "I am drowning," he thought. "But at least my grave will lie near my beloved."

Then all went black inside his head. Wahwee turned him into a brown water rush. He wanted to **torment** the lovers. They would float near each other but never be able to embrace.

torment
cause great pain to

That is not how it turned out. Nerida and Birwain are together forever now. The lilies and the rushes spread until they covered the pool. The lilies live in the center, like an upturned, ruby face. The rushes surround them, lining the banks of the pool. There are so many lilies and rushes now that they rub up against one another. Tall rushes bend over the open faces of the lilies to protect them from stormy winds. If you sit quietly on the bank, you might hear the murmur of their conversation.

WHERE FROST COMES FROM

Maya-Mayi
may uh may ee

Seven gorgeous sisters once walked about the earth. They were known as the **Maya-Mayi**. Long, straight hair flowed down their backs. Their shimmering and sparkling bodies were covered with icicles.

The sisters had a case of wanderlust. They loved to explore new places, even though their parents stayed home. Together they wandered farther and farther away from where they were born. And because there were seven of them, they were not scared. Many tribes tried to befriend the sisters, but they kept to themselves.

Berai-Berai
buh RYE buh RYE

The sisters were skilled hunters. A family of boys, the **Berai-Berai**, loved to watch their long hair fly behind them as they raced forward with spears raised. The Berai-Berai wanted to marry the beautiful sisters and wrap themselves in their long hair. They trailed behind the sisters, camping nearby and leaving presents for them. Sadly for the boys, the sisters barely noticed them. They preferred their own company.

wirrees
(wuhr reez) bark containers

The Berai-Berai had a rare skill: they could find nests of bees and with a special trick get the honey out. They would leave *wirrees* of honey for the Maya-Mayi. The sisters loved the sweet honey, but not the boys who brought it.

The Maya-Mayi were not destined to escape from the desire of men. The clever-man **Wurrunna** stole two of them. When the Berai-Berai discovered two of their beloveds missing, they were broken-hearted. Worse, the five remaining sisters went to live in heaven.

Eventually, the two sisters who had been kidnapped escaped by climbing magic pine trees that grew so tall their tops rose to heaven. When the Berai-Berai learned that now there was no hope of marrying even one of them, they stopped eating. Their tribe offered them many other beautiful girls. They offered them their favorite foods, even a **luscious** nest of ants, but it did no good. The boys grew thinner and thinner, until only their bones showed. They grew pale and hollow and then they died.

The sky spirits had been watching all along. Taking pity on the boys, they brought them up to heaven. There, they hunt bees by day, as they did on earth. And by night, they dance ***corroborees*** sung by the Maya-Mayi. Surely you have seen them— Orion's belt and sword. But to the people of Australia, these stars are just the Berai-Berai, the boys. The boys' camp and the girls' camp are close enough for sharing songs, but not so close that the girls are bothered.

Did you know that sky spirits are always watching you? A relative of the two sisters who escaped from Wurrunna watched him scream in desperation as the sisters rose to heaven. The relative thought Wurrunna's stamping and yelling so funny he began to laugh. He laughed so hard and long he forgot how to stop. Now he is known as the laughing star, for up above us he is laughing even now. Be perfectly quiet tonight and maybe you will hear him.

Wurrunna
wuh RUN nuh

luscious delicious

corroborees
group singings

The Maya-Mayi, the group of stars known as the Pleiades, or Seven Sisters, are still wild girls. They bathe every day, splashing and cavorting like dolphins in the water. They like to play **Bubalarmay**. Whoever makes the loudest splash when she jumps into the water wins. The next time you hear thunder rumbling across the winter sky, you'll know the sisters are at it again. And always afterwards, the rain falls. For where does all that bath water go once it has splashed out of the tub?

The Maya-Mayi miss the earth women they once knew. They shine their cool white light on the earth below as a greeting to all the women there. Once a year, to celebrate the time they once spent on earth, the Maya-Mayi break icicles from their **celestial** bodies. They throw them into space and they hurtle through the night sky. When the people of Australia wake in the morning, they see ice crystals glittering everywhere. They say to one another, "Ah, the Maya-Mayi send greetings! We will show them that we too remember."

With an icicle found on the ground, an Aboriginal mother will numb the septum, or inner ridge, of her small child's nose. When the septum is numb with cold and there is no pain, she will pierce that place. Then the child is ready to have a bone or other ornament placed there. Ever after, that child will know the songs the Maya-Mayi sing.

BIBLIOGRAPHY

General and History

Danielsson, Bengt. *Love in the South Seas.* Translated by F. H. Lyon. Australia: Dominion Press, 1956.

Day, A. Grove, and Carl Stroven, eds. *Best South Sea Stories.* Honolulu: Mutual Publishing, 1964.

Dunford, Betty, and Reilly Ridgell. *Pacific Neighbors: The Islands of Micronesia, Melanesia, and Polynesia.* Honolulu: The Bess Press, 1996.

Faurot, Jeannette, ed. *Asian-Pacific Folktales and Legends.* New York: Touchstone, 1995.

Harstad, James, and Cheryl Harstad. *Asia-Pacific Literature.* Vol. 1-4. State of Hawai'i Department of Education, 1981.

Howe, K. R. *Where the Waves Fall: A New South Sea Islands History from First Settlement to Colonial Rule.* Honolulu: University of Hawai'i Press, 1984.

Howe, K. R., Robert Kiste, and Brij Lal, eds. *Tides of History: The Pacific Islands in the Twentieth Century.* Honolulu: University of Hawai'i Press, 1994.

Kluge, P. F. *The Edge of Paradise: America in Micronesia.* New York: Random House, 1991.

Knappert, Jan. *Pacific Mythology: An Encyclopedia of Myth and Legend.* London: Aquarian/Thorsons, 1992.

Lavill, Jean, and Joseph Berkowitz. *Pacific Island Legends: Life and Legends in the South Pacific Islands.* Noumea, New Caledonia: Librairie Pentecost, 1944.

Poort, W. A. *The Dance in the Pacific.* The Netherlands: Vanderlee Press, 1985.

Ridgell, Reilly. *Pacific Nations and Territories.* 3rd ed. Honolulu: Bess Press, 1995.

Legends and Literature (General)

Austin, Mary C., and Esther C. Jenkins. *Literature for Children and Young Adults About Oceania.* Westport, CT: Greenwood Press, 1996.

Poignant, Roslyn. *Oceanic and Australasian Mythology.* London: Paul Hamlyn Ltd., 1967; reprint, Newnes Books, 1985.

Navigation

Brower, Kenneth. *A Song For Satawal.* New York: Harper & Row, 1983.

Gladwin, Thomas. *East Is a Big Bird: Navigation and Logic on Puluwat Atoll.* Cambridge, MA: Harvard University Press, 1970.

Kyselka, Will. *An Ocean in Mind.* Honolulu: University of Hawai'i Press, 1987.

Lewis, David. *We, the Navigators.* Honolulu: University of Hawai'i Press, 1972.

Thomas, Stephen D. *The Last Navigator.* New York: Ballantine Books, 1987.

MICRONESIA

Alkire, William H. *An Introduction to the Peoples and Cultures of Micronesia.* 2nd ed. Menlo Park, CA: Cummings Publishing Co., 1977.

Ashby, Gene, ed. *Never and Always: Micronesian Legends, Fables and Folklore.* Eugene, OR and Kolonia, Pohnpei: Rainy Day Press, 1989.

————, ed. *Some Things of Value; Micronesian Customs and Beliefs.* Rev. ed. Eugene, OR and Kolonia, Pohnpei: Rainy Day Press, 1985.

Bendure, Glenda, and Ned Friary. *Micronesia: A Lonely Planet Travel Survival Kit.* Berkeley, CA: Lonely Planet Publications, 1995.

Flood, Bo. *From the Mouth of the Monster Eel: Stories from Micronesia.* Golden, CO: Fulcrum Publishing, 1996.

Grey, Eve. *Legends of Micronesia*. Books One and Two. Trust Territory of the Pacific Islands, Office of the High Commissioner, 1951.

Hermes, Jules, *The Children of Micronesia*. Minneapolis: Carolrhoda Books, 1994.

Hezel, Francis X., S. J. *The First Taint of Civilization: A History of the Caroline and Marshall Islands in Pre-Colonial Days, 1521-1885*. Pacific Islands Monograph Series No. 1, University of Hawai'i, Honolulu, 1983.

Hezel, Francis X., S. J., and M. L. Berg. *Micronesia: Winds of Change. A Book of Readings on Micronesian History*. Saipan: Trust Territory of the Pacific Islands, 1980.

Johnson, Margaret, and Roy Johnson, eds. *Life and Legends of Micronesia*. Murfreesboro, NC: Johnson Publishing Company, 1980.

Mitchell, Roger E., *Micronesian Folktales*. Nagoya, Japan: Asian Folklore Institute, 1973.

Peck, Dr. William. *A Tidy Universe of Islands*. Honolulu: Mutual Publishing, 1997.

Reiter, Paul (coordinator). Micronesian Legends and Culture. Precision Teaching Summer Institute, Guam, 1971.

Salas, Marilyn, and Debbie Tkel. *A Bibliography of Literature for Micronesian Children*. Project BEAM, University of Guam, 1991.

Skinner, Mark E. *Contemporary Micronesian Literature: A Preliminary Bibliography*. Barrigada, Guam, 1990.

Stanley, David. *Micronesia Handbook*. Chico, California: Moon Publications, 1989.

Mariana Islands

Arago, Jacques Etienne Victor. *Narrative of a Voyage Round the World in the Uranie and Physicienne Corvettes Commanded by Captain Freycinet During the Years 1817, 1818, 1819, and 1920*. 2 vol. reprint, New York: Da Capo Press, 1971.

Farrell, Don. *History of the Northern Mariana Islands*. Public School System, Commonwealth of the Northern Mariana Islands, 1991.

_____. *Tinian*. Edited by Phyllis Koontz. Tinian, MP: Micronesian Publications, 1989.

Fritz, Georg. *The Chamorro: A History and Ethnography of the Mariana Islands*. Edited by Scott Russell. Translated by Elfriede Craddock. Saipan: Division of Historic Preservation, 1989.

Hezel, Francis X., S. J. *From Conquest to Colonialization: Spain in the Mariana Islands, 1690-1740*. Saipan: Division of Historic Preservation, 1989.

Peck, W. M. *I Speak the Beginning: Anthology of Surviving Poetry of the Northern Mariana Islands*. Commonwealth Council for Arts and Culture, 1982.

Political Status Education Coordinating Commission. *Hale-ta: Hestorian Taotao Tano,* History of the Chamorro People. Agana, Guam, 1993.

Shewman, Richard, ed. *Umanidat: A Journal of the Humanities*. Vol. 4. Saipan: Diocese of Chalan Kanoa, 1996.

Wernhart, Karl R. "A Preliminary Manuscript Record of the Chamorro, Micronesia." *Journal of Pacific History* 7 (1972).

Guam

Chamorro Language and Cultural Program. *Legends*. Agana, Guam: Department of Education, 1985.

Legends of Guam. Collected by Staff of Nieves M. Flores Memorial Library and the Guam Museum, 1972.

Major, Cat. *Myths of Guam.* Sacramento, CA, 1987.

School of Nursing, Class of 1951. Taotaomonas. Micronesian Area Research Center Collection. Tamuning, Guam: Guam Memorial Hospital, 1949.

Thompson, Laura Maud. *Guam and Its People. With a Village Journal by Jesus C. Barcinas.* Westport, CT: Greenwood Press, 1969.

Torres, J. "Why the Central Part of Guam is Narrow." *Guam Recorder,* 11 Feb. 1937.

Torres, Robert Tenorio. "Selected Marianas Folklore, Legend, Literature: A Critical Commentary." MS Thesis, San Diego State University, 1991.

University of Guam, Education 453. Legend of the Breadfruit Tree. Micronesian Area Research Center Collection, Agana, Guam, 1962.

Palau

Alonz, Laetitia. *A Collection of Palauan Legends.* Koror, Palau: Palau Press Agency, 1990.

_____. *A Collection of Palauan Legends.* Vol. 1 & 2. Illustrated by Jerome Esebei Temengil. Koror, Republic of Palau: Island 21st Century Publications, 1995.

Barbour, Nancy. *Palau.* San Francisco: Full Court Press, 1990.

Briones, Reuben, and Jerome Temengil. *Legends of Palau.* MB Pacific Enterprises, 1991.

Gordon, Maura. *Conservation Practices and Ethics of Palau.* Palau Resource Institute.

Hijakata, Hisakatsu. *Collected Works.* Edited by Sudo Ken'ichi. Sasakawa Peace Foundation, Japan, 1997.

_____. *Stone Images of Palau.* University of Guam, Micronesian Area Research Center, #3, Agana, Guam, 1973.

Parmentier, Richard J. *The Sacred Remains: Myth, History and Polity in Belau.* Chicago: University of Chicago Press, 1987.

Telmetang, Marciana. *Bai.* Edited by Faustina Rehuher. Belau National Museum, 1993.

Marshall Islands

Buckingham, H. W., Lcdr., CMC, USN. Collection of Stories From the Marshall Islands, n.d.

Davenport, W. H. "Marshallese Folklore Types." *Journal of American Folklore* 66 (261), 1953.

_____. "Fourteen Marshallese Riddles." *Journal of American Folklore* 65 (257), 1952.

Downing, Jane, Dirk H. R. Spennemann, and Margaret Bennett, eds. *Bwebwenatoon Etto: A Collection of Marshallese Legends and Traditions.* Marshall Islands Culture and History, Series E: Legends, Chants and Proverbs, Majuro, Republic of the Marshall Islands, Historic Preservation Office, 1992.

La Bedbedin. *Man this Reef.* Translated by Gerald Knight. Micronitor News and Print, Majuro, RMI, 1982.

Yap

Burrows, Edwub Grant. *Flower In My Ear: Arts and Ethos of Ifaluk Atoll.* Seattle: University of Washington Press, 1963.

Chuggen, John. *Yapese Legends.* Yap State Department of Education, 1996.

Lessa, W. A. *More Tales from Ulithi Atoll: A Content Analysis.* Berkeley: University of California Press, 1980.

Lessa, W. A. *Tales from Ulithi Atoll.* Berkeley: University of California Press, 1961.

Mangefel, John A. *Seven Legends of Yap.* Yap State Department of Education, 1970.

Uag, Raphael. Yapese History (Legends), Yap, 1968.

Chuuk

Hall, Edward T., and Karl J. Pelzer. *The Economy of the Truk Islands: An Anthropological and Economic Survey.* Honolulu: U.S. Commercial Company, Economic Survey, 1946.

Mitchell, Roger E. "A Study of the Cultural, Historical, and Acculturative Factors Influencing the Repertories of Two Trukese Informants." Ph.D. diss., Folklore Institute, Indiana University, 1967.

Pohnpei

Ashby, Gene. *Pohnpei: An Island Argosy.* Eugene, OR and Kolonia, Pohnpei: Rainy Day Press, 1993.

Ehrlich, Paul Mark. "'The Clothes of Men': Ponape Island and German Colonial Rule, 1899-1914." Ph.D. diss., State University of New York, 1978.

Hanlon, David L., "Upon A Stone Altar: A History of the Island of Ponape from the Beginnings of Foreign Contact to 1890," Ph.D. diss., University of Hawai'i-Manoa, 1984.

Morrill, Sibley S. *Ponape: Where American Colonialism Confronts Black Magic, Five Kingdoms, and the Mysterious Ruins of Nan Madol.* San Francisco: Cadleon Press, 1970.

Kosrae

Lewis, James L. *Kusaien Acculturation, 1824-1948.* Saipan: Trust Territory, 1967.

O'Brien, Ilma E. "Cultural Continuity and Conversion on the Eastern Carolines: A Study of Interaction Between Islanders and Christian Missionaries in Ponape and Kosrae." Ph.D. diss., La Trobe University, 1979.

Peoples, James Gregory. "Deculturation and Dependence in a Micronesian Community." Ph.D. diss., U.C. Davis, 1977.

Ritter, Lynn Takata, and Philip L. Ritter. *The European Discovery of Kosrae Island.* Saipan: Historic Preservation Office, Trust Territory, 1982.

Wilson, Walter Scott. Outline of Kusaien History. n.d.

Kiribati

Grimble, Arthur. *Tungaru Traditions: Writings on the Atoll Culture of the Gilbert Islands.* Edited by H. E. Maude. Honolulu: University of Hawai'i Press, 1989.

Koru, Peter Kanere, and Ginette Sullivan, eds. *Iango mai Kiribati: Stories From Kiribati.* Kiribati Extension Centre, Tarawa, Kiribati, and Institute of Pacific Studies, University of the South Pacific, Suva, Fiji, 1986.

MELANESIA

Chowning, Ann. *An Introduction to the Peoples and Cultures of Melanesia.* 2nd ed. Menlo Park, CA: Cummings Publishing Co., 1973.

Codrington, R. H. *The Melanesians: Studies in Their Anthropology and Folk-Lore.* Oxford: Clarendon Press, 1891.

Papua New Guinea

Gill, William Wyatt. *The South Pacific and New Guinea.* Sydney: Charles Potter, 1892.

McCarthy, Jack. *Legends of Papua New Guinea.* Adelaide, Australia: Rigby Limited, 1973.

Young, Michael W. *Magicians of Manumanua: Living Myth in Kalauna.* Berkeley: University of California Press, 1983.

Solomon Islands

Bauman, Kay. *Solomon Island Folktales from Malaita.* Danbury, CT: Rutledge Books, 1998.

Branham, Mary Edith, and Joel S. Branham. *Bed The Turtle Softly: Legends of the South Pacific.* Mukilteo, WA: Scott Publications, 1975.

Foliga, N., M. Haebiru, T. Iono, K. Suifalu, and D. Daununu. *The Large Hungry Eel and Other Animal Stories by Solomon Islanders.* Honiara, B. S. I. P.: Solomon Islands Catholic Association, 1973.

Kirtley, Bacil F., and Samuel H. Elbert. "Animal Tales from Rennell and Bellona." *Journal of the Polynesian Society* 82 (3, 1973): 245-265.

Wheeler, Gerald Camden. "Mono-Alu Folklore (Bougainville Strait, Western Solomon Islands)." DSc thesis, University of London, 1926.

Vanuatu

Facey, Ellen E. *Nguna Voices: Text and Culture from Central Vanuatu.* Calgary, Alberta: The University of Calgary Press, 1988.

POLYNESIA

Andersen, Johannes C. *Myths and Legends of the Polynesians.* London: Harrap, 1928; reprint New York: Dover Publishing, 1995.

Branham, Mary Edith, and Joel S. Branham. *Bed The Turtle Softly: Legends of the South Pacific.* Mukilteo, WA: Scott Publications, 1975.

Luomala, Katherine, *Voices on the Wind: Polynesian Myths and Chants,* Bishop Museum Press, Honolulu, Hawaii, 1955.

Samoa

Muse, Corey, and Shirley Muse. *The Birds and the Birdlore of Samoa.* Washington: Pioneer Press, 1982.

Stuebel C. *Myths and Legends of Samoa: Tala o le Vavau.* Translated by Brother Herman. Wellington, NZ: AH & AW Reedy, 1976.

Wendt, Albert. Leaves of the Banyan Tree. Talanoa, Hawai'i, 1979.

Tonga

Gifford, Edward W. *Tongan Myths and Tales.* Bernice Bishop Museum, Bayard Dominick Expedition, Publication #8, 1924.

Pitcairn Island

McKinny, Sam. *Bligh: A True Account of Mutiny Aboard His Majesty's Ship Bounty.* Camden, ME: International Marine Publishing Co., 1989.

Shapiro, Harry L. *The Heritage of the Bounty,* Garden City, NY: Anchor Books, 1962.

Wahlroos, Sven. *Mutiny and Romance in the South Seas: A Companion to the Bounty Adventure,* Topsfield, MA: Salem House, 1989.

Easter Island

McCall, Grant. *Rapanui: Tradition and Survival on Easter Island.* Honolulu: University of Hawai'i Press, 1981.

Métraux, Alfred. *Ethnology of Easter Island.* Bishop Museum Bulletin 160, Honolulu, Hawai'i, 1971.

Hawaiian Islands

Alameida, Roy Kākula. *Nā Mo'olelo Hawai'i o ka Wā Kahiko: Stories of Old Hawai'i.* Honolulu: The Bess Press, 1997.

Beamer, Nona. *Talking Story with Nona Beamer.* Honolulu: The Bess Press, 1984.

Beckwith, Martha Warren. *Hawaiian Mythology.* Honolulu: University of Hawai'i Press, 1970.

————. *The Kumulipo: A Hawaiian Creation Chant.* Honolulu: University of Hawai'i Press, 1972.

Colum, Padraic. *Legends of Hawaii.* New Haven: Yale University Press, 1937.

Cronin, Gloria L., ed. *Tales of Molokai.* University of Hawai'i Press, 1992.

Day, A. Grove, and Carl Stroven, eds. *A Hawaiian Reader.* Honolulu: Mutual Publishing, 1959.

Dunford, Betty. *The Hawaiians of Old.* Honolulu: The Bess Press, 1980.

Kalakaua, King David. *The Legends and Myths of Hawaii.* Honolulu: Mutual Publishing, 1990.

London, Jack. *Stories of Hawaii.* Honolulu: Mutual Publishing, 1986.

_____. *Tales of Hawaii.* Honolulu: Press Pacifica, 1984.

Luomala, Katharine. *Hawaiian Puppetry.* Lā'ie, Hawai'i: Institute for Polynesian Studies, Brigham Young University-Hawai'i, 1984.

Maguire, Eliza D. *Kona Legends.* Hawai'i: Petroglyph Press, 1966.

Summers, Catherine C. *Molokai: A Site Survey.* #14. Pacific Anthropological Record, Bishop Museum Press, Honolulu, 1971.

Thompson, Vivian L.. *Hawaiian Legends of Tricksters and Riddlers.* Honolulu: Kolowalu Press, 1969.

_____. *Hawaiian Myths of Earth, Sea, and Sky.* Honolulu: Kolowalu Press, 1988.

_____. *Hawaiian Tales of Heroes and Champions.* Kolowalu Press, 1986.

Tune, Suelyn Ching. *Maui and the Secret of Fire.* Honolulu: University of Hawai'i Press, 1991.

Williams, Julie Stewart. *And the Birds Appeared.* Honolulu: University of Hawai'i Press, 1988.

New Zealand (Maori)

Orbell, Margaret. *Maori Folktales in Maori and English.* New Zealand: Blackwood and Janet Paul Ltd, 1968.

AUSTRALIA

Cowan, James. *Mysteries of the Dream-Time: The Spiritual Life of Australian Aborigines.* Dorset, England: Prism Press, 1989.

Ellis, Jean A. *From the Dreamtime.* Victoria, Australia: Collins Dove, 1991.

Lawlor, Robert. *Voices of the First Day: Awakening in the Aboriginal Dreamtime.* Rochester, Vermont: Inner Traditions International, 1991.

Lawrie, Margaret. *Myths and Legends of Torres Strait.* New York: Taplinger Publishing Company, 1971.

McConnel, Ursula. *Myths of the Munkan* (on Torres Straits Islands, Australia). Victoria, Australia: Melbourne University Press, 1957.

Mountford, Charles P. *The Dawn of Time.* Adelaide: Rigby Limited, 1969.

_____. *The Dreamtime.* Adelaide: Rigby Limited, 1965.

_____, Charles P. *The First Sunrise.* Adelaide: Rigby Limited, 1971.

Parker, K. Langloh. *Australian Legendary Tales.* New York: The Viking Press, 1966.

_____. *Wise Women of the Dreamtime: Aboriginal Tales of the Ancestral Powers.* Rochester, Vermont: Inner Traditions International, 1993.

Robinson, Roland. *The Feathered Serpent.* Sydney: Edwards and Shaw, 1956.